PRĀṆĀYĀMA RAHASYA

(SECRETS OF PRĀṆĀYĀMA)

with scientific factual evidence

Illustrated-authoritative exposition of self-tried experiments of prāṇāyāma, meditation and awakening of serpent-power

Swami Ramdev

Divya Prakashan
Divya Yog Mandir (Trust)
Patanjali Yogpeeth, Hardwar

II OM II

Publisher : **Divya Prakashan**
Divya Yog Mandir (Trust)
Patanjali Yogpeeth
Maharishi Dayanand Gram,
Delhi-Hardwar Highway, Bahadarabad,
Hardwar-249402 (Uttarakhand)
E-mail : divyayoga@rediffmail.com
Website : www.divyayoga.com
Phone : 01334-244107, 240008, 246737
Fax : 01334-244805

First Edition : 50000 copies

Revised Edition : March 2009

Printed by : **Sai Security Printers Pvt. Ltd.**
SCO-63, HUDA Market, Sector-31,
Faridabad-121003 (Haryana)
Tel. : 0129-4194900
E-mail: sspdel@saiprinters.com

ISBN 978-81-89235-01-7

English
620 (11-16)

Contents

Introduction to the Coloured Pictures given in the beginning of the book

Sl. No.	Topic
Pic-1	Uḍḍīyāna-bandha
Pic-2	Anuloma-viloma Prāṇāyāma
Pic-3	Anuloma-viloma Prāṇāyāma
Pic-4	Bhrāmarī Prāṇāyāma
Pic-5	Mūlādhāra Cakra
Pic-6	Svādhiṣṭhāna Cakra
Pic-7	Maṇipūra Cakra
Pic-8	Hṛdaya Cakra
Pic-9	Anāhata Cakra
Pic-10	Viśuddhi Cakra
Pic-11	Sauṣumṇa-jyoti
Pic-12	Cakra Darśana
Pic-13	Divya-dṛṣṭi
Pic-14	Piṅgalā-Gaṇḍamālā & Organs of Suṣumṇa
Pic-15	Gāyatrī Dhyāna
Pic-16	Divine Vision-Meditation Vision & realisation of 'Om Brahma'

Pic-1 : Uḍḍīyāna-bandha

Pic-2 : Anuloma-viloma Prāṇāyāma

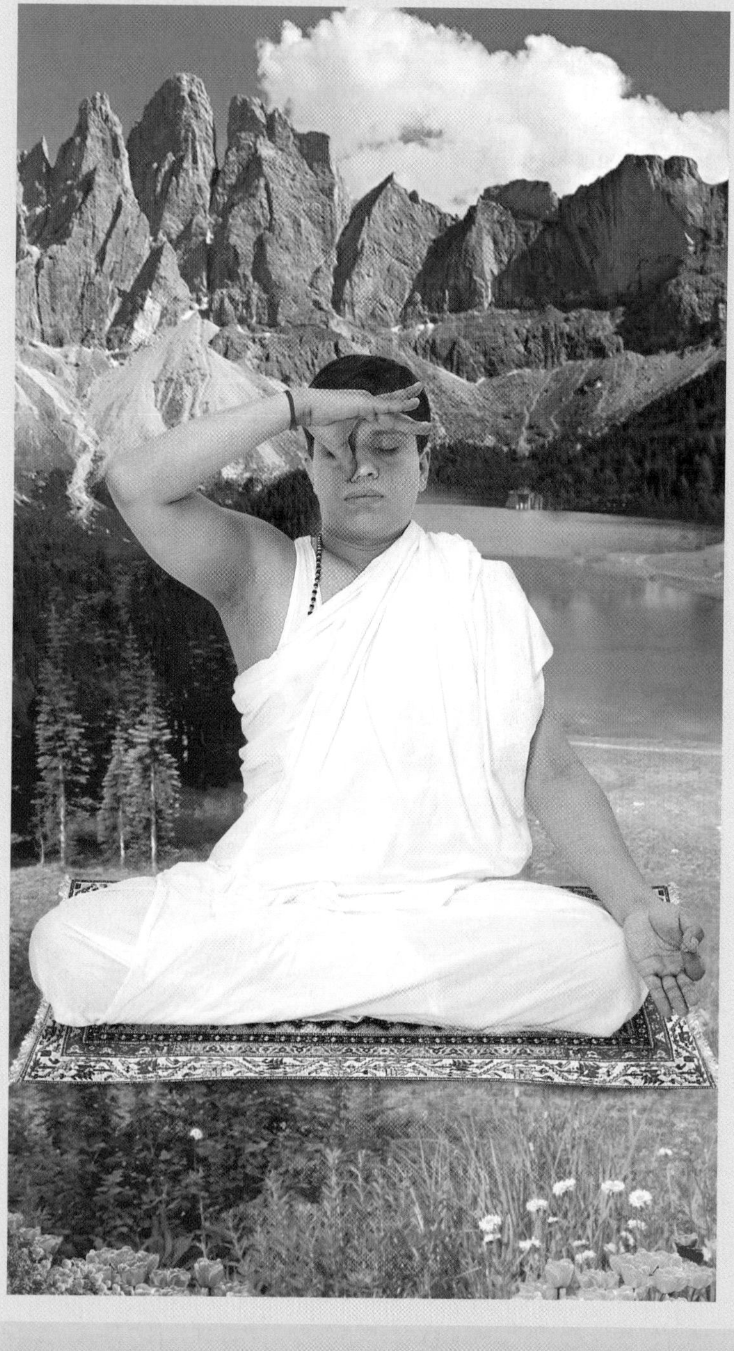

Pic-3 : Anuloma-viloma Prāṇāyāma

Pic-4 : Bhrāmarī Prāṇāyāma

Pic-5 : Mūlādhāra Cakra

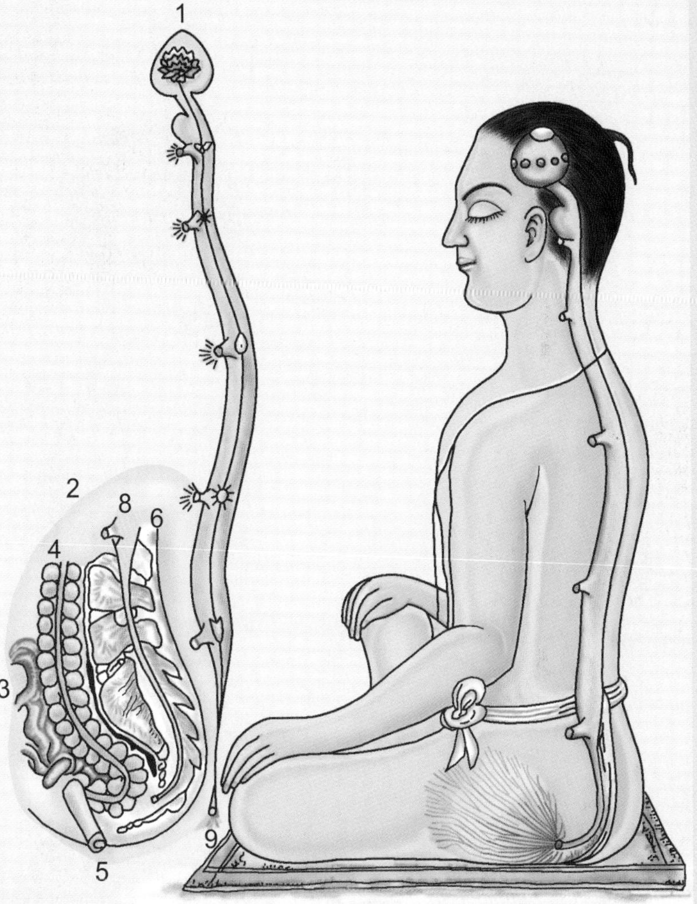

Pic-6 : Svādhiṣṭhāna Cakra

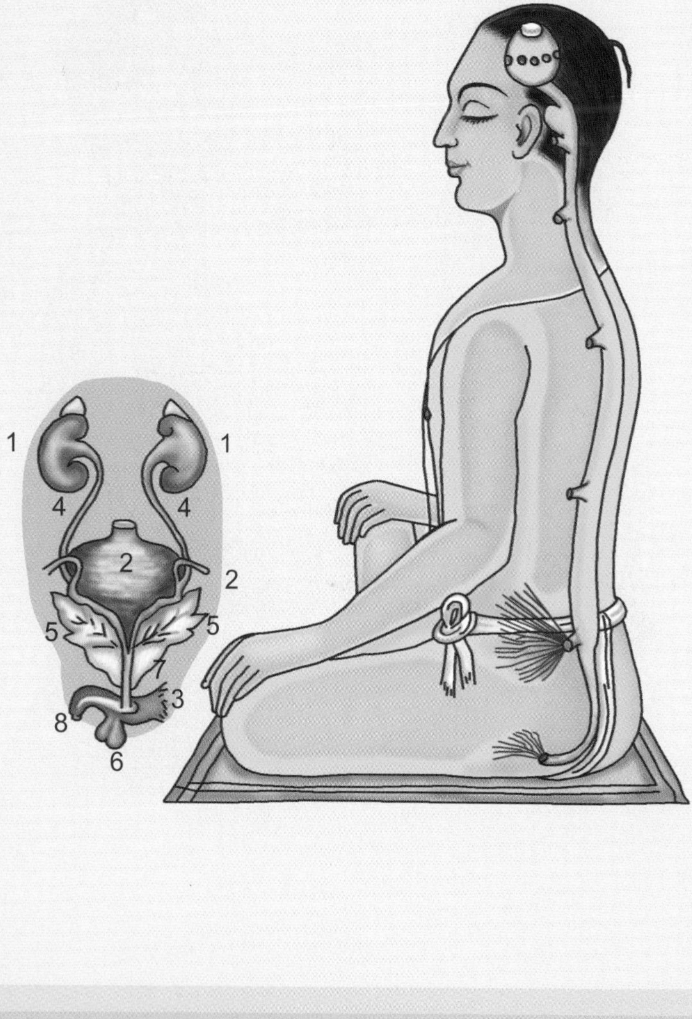

Pic-7 : Maṇipūra Cakra

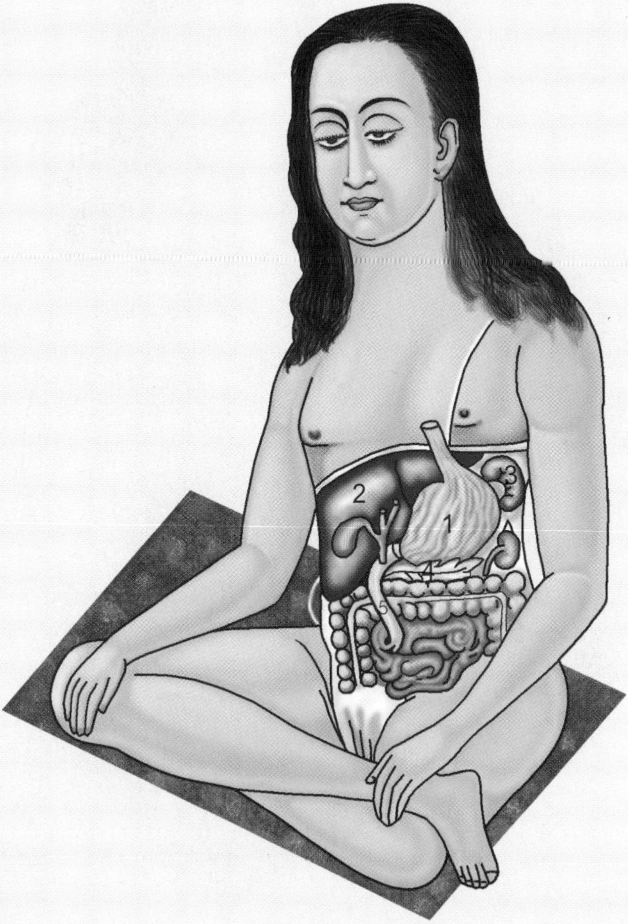

Pic-8 : Hṛdaya Cakra

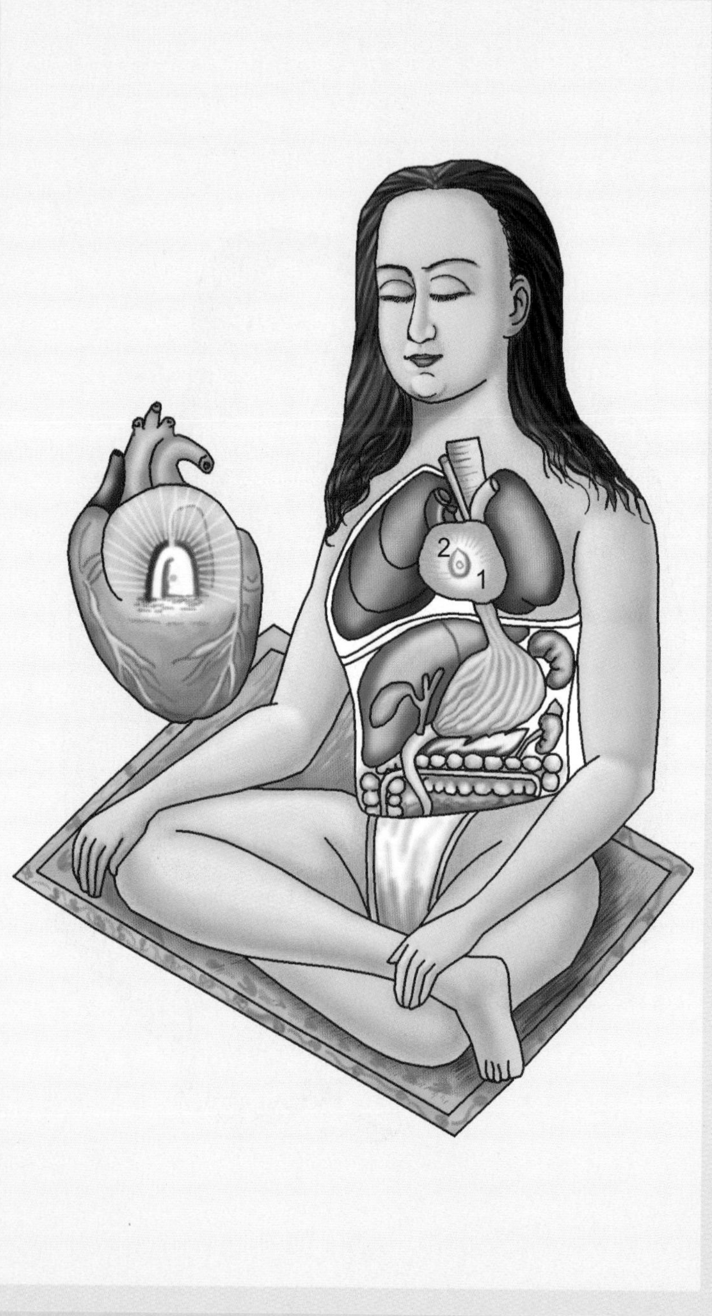

Pic-9 : Anāhata Cakra

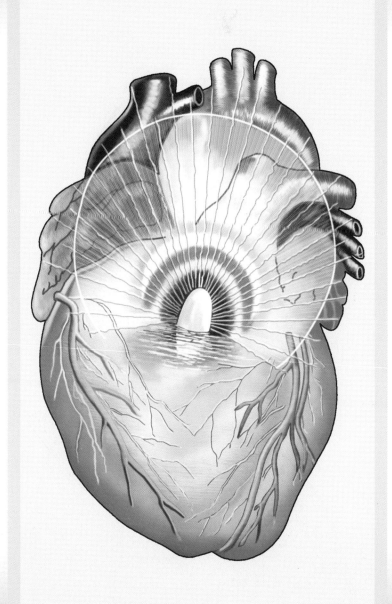

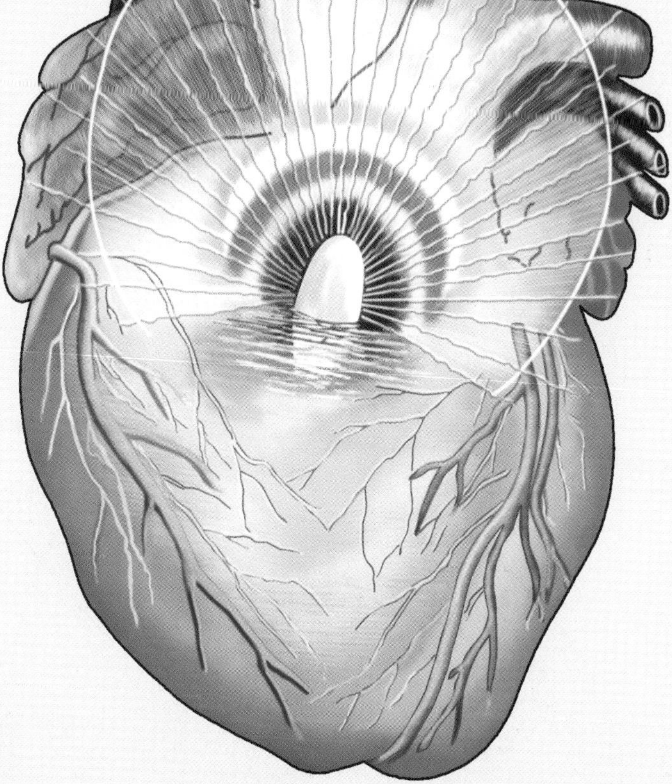

Pic-10 : Viśuddhi Cakra

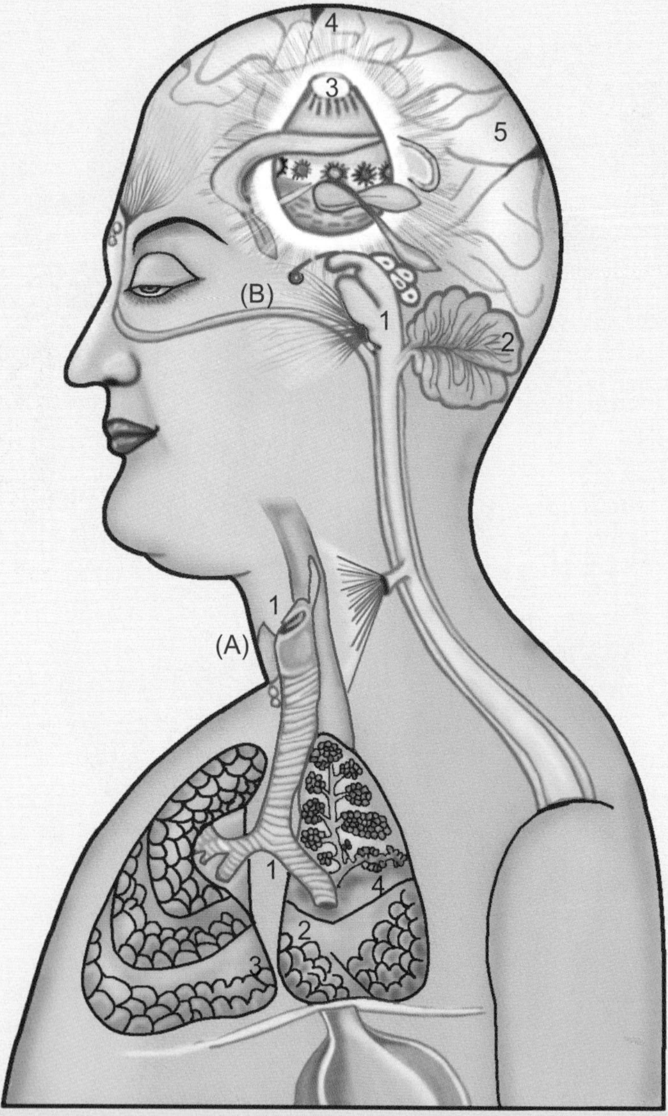

Pic-11 : Sauṣumṇa-jyoti

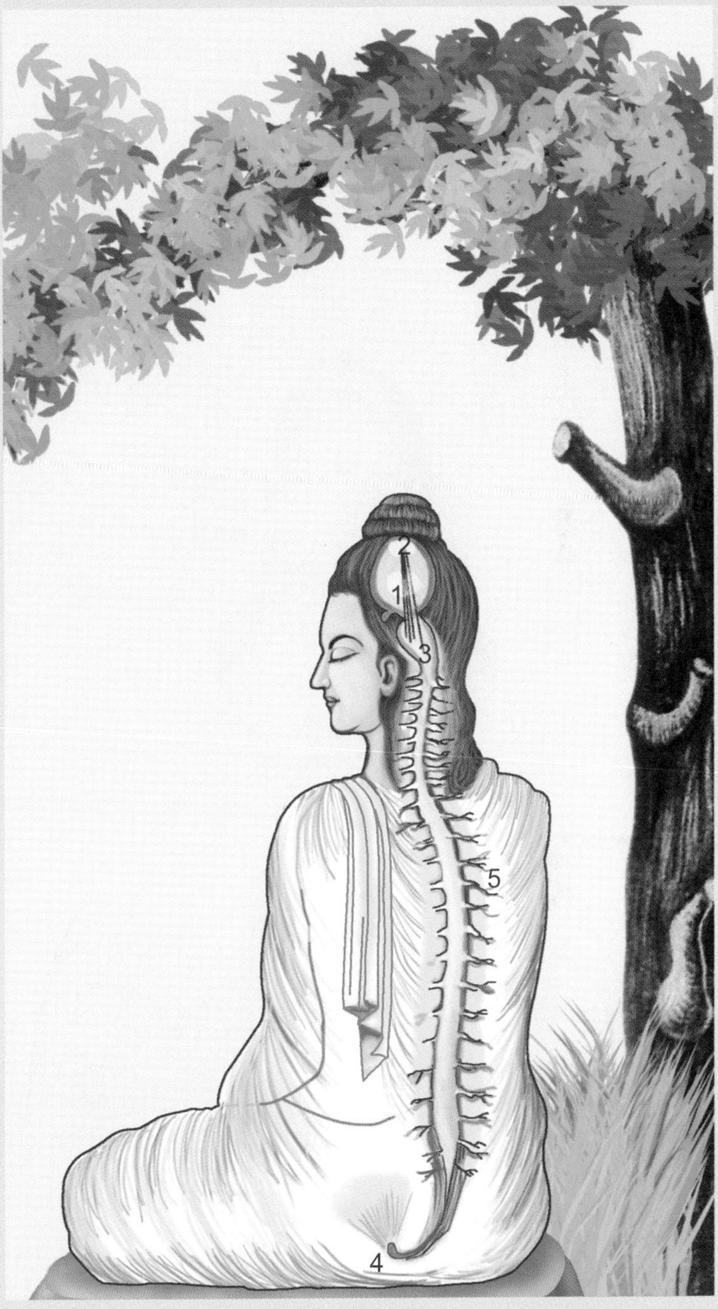

Pic-12 : Cakra Darśana

Pic-13 : Divya-dṛṣṭi

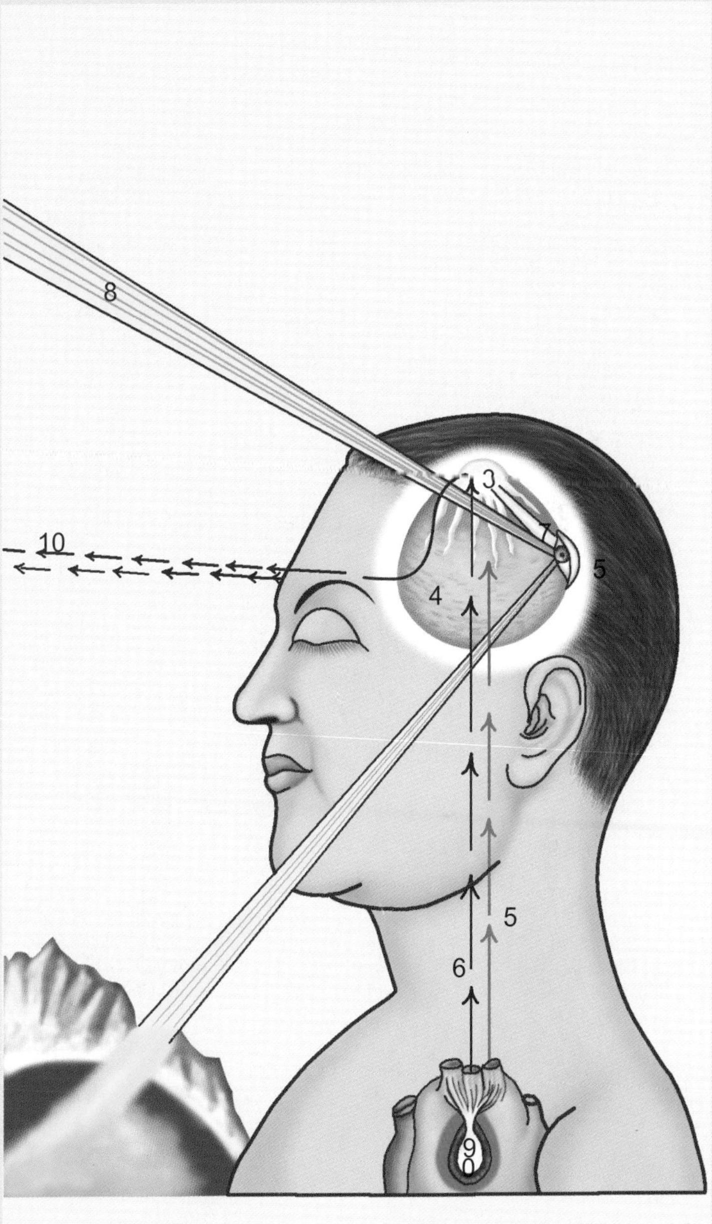

Pic-14 : Piṅgalā-Gaṇḍamālā & Organs of Suṣumṇa

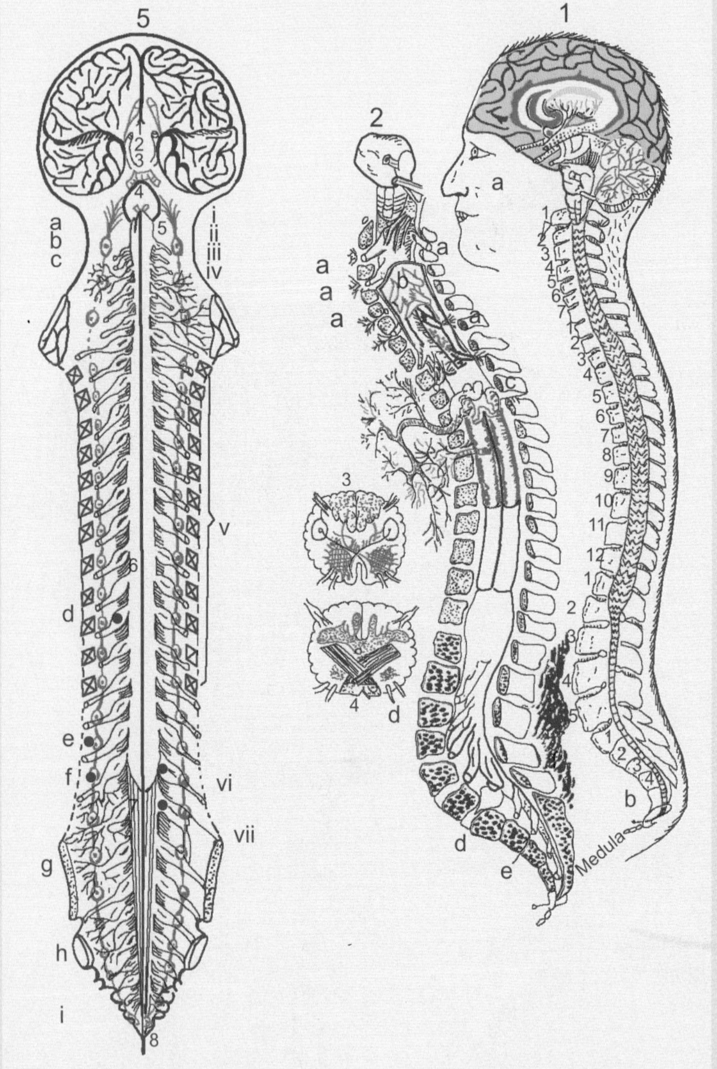

Pic-15 : Gāyatrī Dhyāna

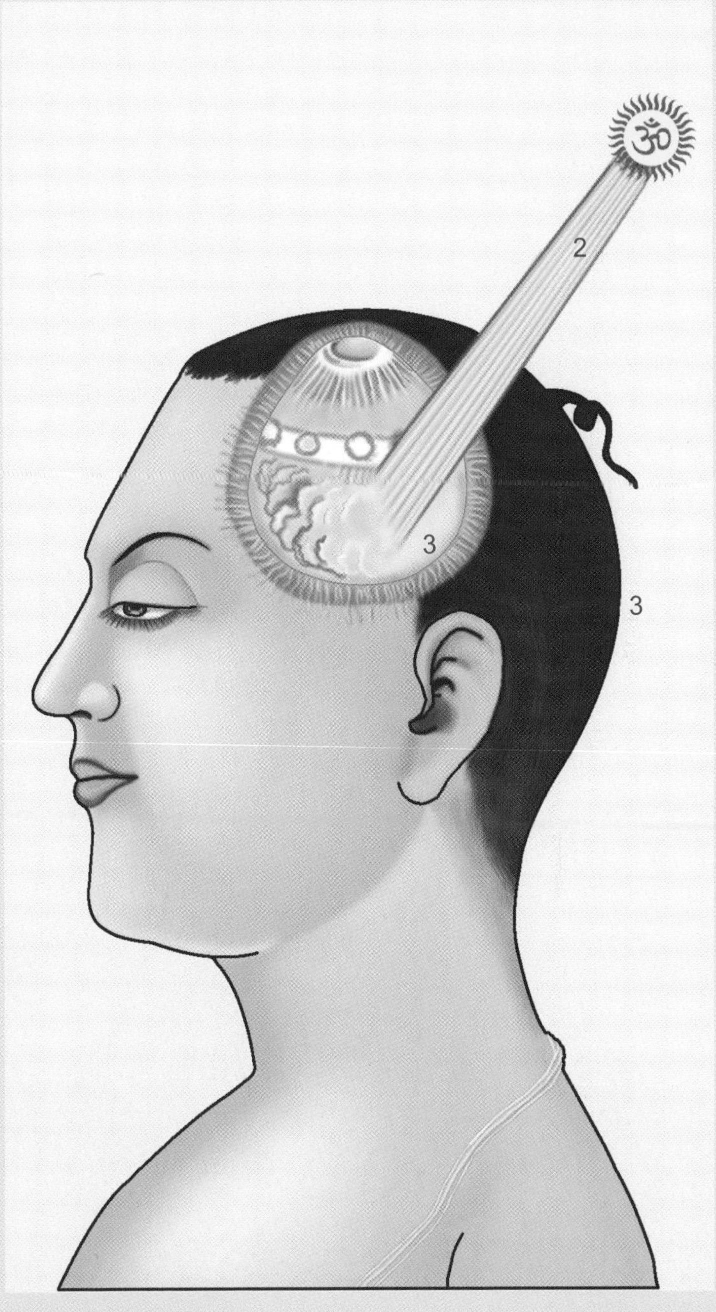

Pic-16 : Divine Vision-Meditation
Vision & realisation of 'Om Brahma'

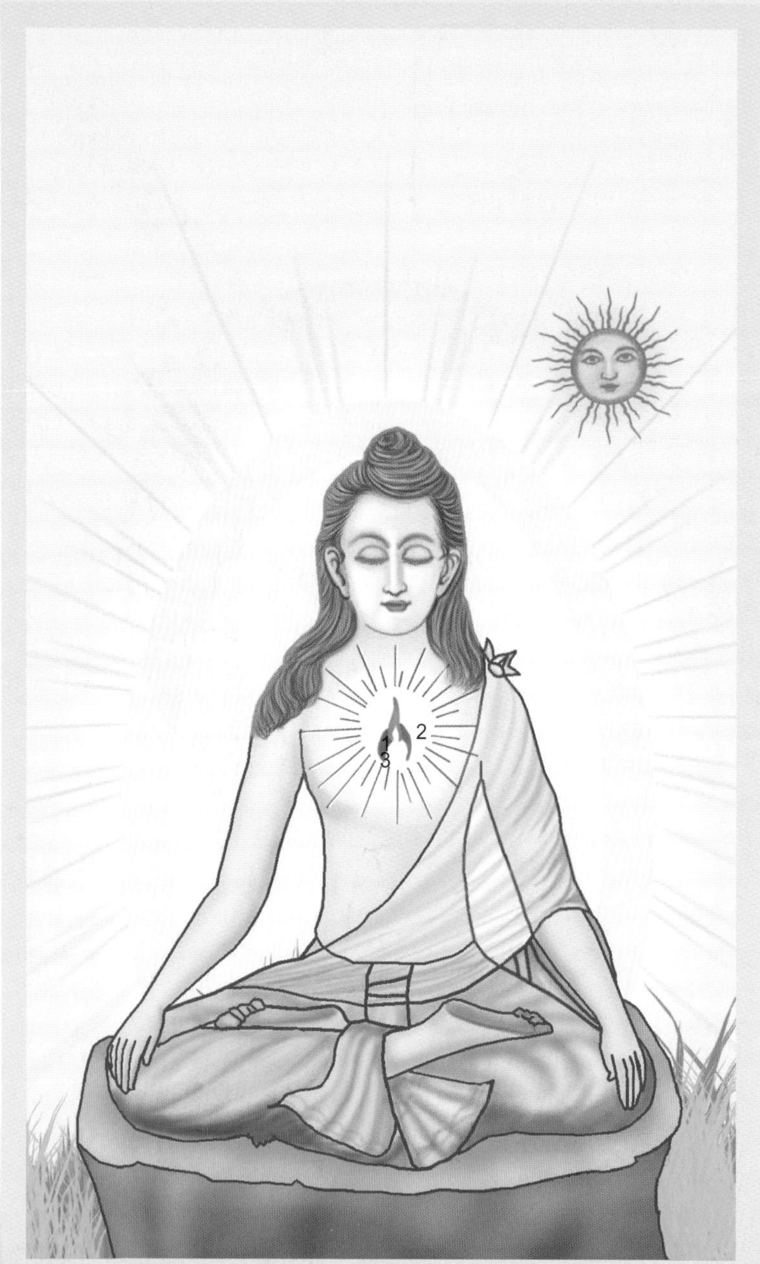

FOREWORD

dharmārthakāmamokṣāṇāmārogyaṁ mūlamuttamam /
rogāstasyāpahartāraḥ śreyaso jīvitasya vā //

(CARAKA SŪTRASTHĀNA 1.15)

It is extremely essential to be completely healthy to attain the four goals of human endeavour, viz., observance of religious duties, earning money, begetting progeny with a pure and noble intention, and attaining liberation. There is hardly any hope of happiness, peace and bliss when the body is disease-ridden. No matter one possesses every thing–name, fame, wealth, opulence, affluence, near and dear ones, his body is no more than a corpse if there is no proper blood circulation in it, the limbs are not strong and supple, and the sinews have no strength and energy. Ayurveda has emerged to make mankind achieve healthy body and healthy mind, and it continues to render this great service. With a view to removing the internal impurities and disorders of the body and attaining complete bliss through samādhi by purifying the inner conscience, sages, savants and accomplished yogis have invented yogic procedures. Prāṇāyāma occupies the pride of place among yogic procedures. The sage Patañjali has propounded aṣṭāṅga (eight- limbed) yoga for the benefit of mankind. It comprises abstinences (yama), observances (niyama) and yogic postures (āsana) as external (bahiraṅga) yoga which helps purge and purify the body and the mind.

Concentration (dhāraṇā), meditation (dhyāna) and transcendental trance (samādhi) fall under internal (antaraṅga) yoga which are the means to the attainment of self-elevation and bliss of liberated existence (kaivalya). Prāṇāyāma serves as a bridge between external and internal yoga. If one has to make the body healthy and disease-free, or one has to purge the body and purify the soul, it is possible only by doing prāṇāyāma. It is only by restraining impulses (vṛttis) and by getting established in the self that a seeker (sādhaka) can attain liberated existence.

In the holy presence of the Revered Yogarṣi Swami Ramdevji Maharaj, the Founder Chairman of Divya Yog Mandir Trust,

Kankhal, and Patanjali Yogpeeth, Hardwar, lacs of learners every year receive practical training of the specific procedures of yoga, like prāṇāyāma, meditation etc., and get rid of ailments of the body and disorders of the mind. I express my heart-felt gratitude to revered Acharya Shri Pradyumnaji Maharaj, Ārṣa Gurukul, Khanpur, Dr. Vijaypal 'Pracetāḥ', Jaipur, Acharya Satyajit, Ajmer, Dr. Jawahar Pal, Narnaul, Shri V. Raghavan, the esteemed Chairman of Sai Printing Press, Faridabad, to whom goes the credit of extending his full support and cooperation in seeing this book in its present beautiful form and get-up.

We hope that this latest edition of the book, backed by a lot of scientific evidence, will be of immense interest to our discerning readers.

–ACHARYA BALKRISHNA

PRĀṆA-SŪKTA (ATHARVA 11/4/1-26)

prāṇāya namo yasya sarvamidaṁ vaśe /
yo bhūtaḥ sarvasyeśvaro yasmintsarvaṁ pratiṣṭhitam //1//

[yasya vaśe] under whose control [idaṁ sarvaṁ] all this world is, to that [prāṇaya namaḥ] prāṇa, is my salutation. [yaḥ sarvasya īśvaraḥ] the prāṇa, the lord of all [bhūtaḥ] is and [yasmin sarvaṁ pratiṣṭhitam] in which all things are happening.

namaste prāṇa krandāya namaste stanayitnave /
namaste prāṇa vidyute namaste prāṇa varṣate //2//

O Prāṇa! [krandāya te namaḥ] obeisance to thee, roaring one [stanayitnave] obeisance to thee, thundering in the clouds. O Prāṇa! [vidyute] obeisance to thee who lights up in lightning and O Prāṇa! [varṣate] obeisance to thee who rains.

yat prāṇa stanayitnunā ' bhikrandatyoṣadhiḥ /
pra vīyante garbhāndadhate ' tho bahvīrvi jāyante //3//

O Prāṇa! [yat stanayitnunā oṣadhiḥ abhikrandati] when, in the form of clouds, you thunder loudly before the (medicinal) plants, when the plants [pra vīyante] become radiant, [garbhān dadhate] become pregnant and [atho bahvīḥ vijāyante] grow and expand in many ways.

yat prāṇa ṛtāvāgate'bhikrandatyoṣadhiḥ /
sarvaṁ tadā pra modate yatkim ca bhūmyāmadhi //4//

O Prāṇa! [ṛtau āgate] when rains set in, you [oṣadhīḥ abhikrandati] start roaring and thundering for the sake of plants; [tadā yat kiṁ ca bhūmyāṁ adhi tat sarvaṁ pra modate] then everything on the earth rejoices.

yadā prāṇo abhyavarṣīdvarṣeṇa pṛthivīṁ mahīm /
paśavastatpra modante maho vai no bhaviṣyati //5//

[yadā praṇaḥ] when prāṇa [varṣeṇa mahīm pṛthivīṁ abhyavarṣīt] rains on this vast earth by showers, [tat paśavaḥ pra modante] then all the creatures rejoice (and think that) they now definitely [naḥ vai mahaḥ bhaviṣyati] will grow and prosper.

abhivṛṣṭā oṣadhayaḥ prāṇena samavādiran /
āyurvai naḥ prātītaraḥ sarvāṁ naḥ surabhīrakaḥ //6//

[abhivṛṣṭāḥ oṣadhayaḥ] after the rains have fallen on plants, they [prāṇena samavādiran] speak to prāṇa, O Prāṇa! [maḥ āyuḥ vai prātitaraḥ] you have enhanced our life [surabhīh] full of fragrance [akaḥ] have done (us all).

namaste astvāyate namo astu parāyate /
namaste prāṇa tiṣṭhata āsīnāyota te namaḥ //7//

[āyate te namaḥ astu] obeisance to the prāṇa that comes in, [parāyate namaḥ astu] obeisance to the prāṇa that goes out. O Prāṇa! [tiṣṭhate] to the one that stands still and [āsīnāya te namaḥ] and obeisance to the prāṇa that sits.

namaste prāṇa prāṇate namo astvapānate /
parācīnāya te namaḥ pratīcīnāya te namaḥ sarvasmai ta idaṁ namaḥ //8//

O Prāṇa! [prāṇate te namaḥ] obeisance to you who run the life [apānate te namaḥ] obeisance to you who perform the apāna (function). [paracīnāya te namaḥ] obeisance to you who move forward and [pratīcīnāya te namaḥ] who move backward. [sarvasmai te idaṁ namaḥ] here is my salutation to you who perform all the functions.

yā te prāṇa priyā tanūryo te prāṇa preyasī /
atho yadbheṣajaṁ tava tasya no dhehi jīvase //9//

O Prāṇa! [yā te priyā tanūḥ] the prāṇa-charged dear body that you have, [yā te preyasī] and the dear parts that you have in the form of prāṇa and apāna, and [atho yat tava bheṣajam] the medicine you have [jīvase naḥ dhehi] give us (that) for a long life.

prāṇah prajā anu vaste pitā putramiva priyam /
prāṇo ha sarvasyśevaro yacca prāṇati yacca na //10//

[pita priyam putram iva] as a father lives with his dear son, like that [prāṇaḥ prajāḥ anu vaste] prāṇa lives with all people. [yat prāṇati] those who have life and [yat ca na] those who are lifeless, [prāṇah sarvasya īsvaraḥ] it is prāṇa who is the lord of them all.

prāṇo mṛtyuḥ prāṇastakmā prāṇaṁ devā upāsate /
prāṇo ha satyavādinamuttame loka ā dadhat //11//

[prāṇaḥ mṛtyuḥ] prāṇa only is death and [prāṇaḥ takmāḥ] prāṇa only is the energy of life. Therefore [prāṇam devaḥ upāsate] all gods worship prāṇa. [prāṇaḥ ha satyavādinam] because it is prāṇa only to a truthful person [uttame loke ā dadhat] provides sustenance in the supreme sphere.

prāṇo virāṭ prāṇo deṣṭrī prāṇaṁ sarve upāsate /
prāṇo ha sūryaścandramāḥ prāṇamāhuḥ prajāpatim //12//

prāṇa is (vi-rāj) extraordinarily radiant and prāṇa only (deṣṭrī) is the motivator of all, therefore [prāṇam sarve upāsate] prāṇa only is worshipped by all. [prāṇaḥ ha sūryaḥ candramāḥ] prāṇa is the sun and the moon and [prāṇam āhuḥ prajāpatim] prāṇa is also called prajāpati.

prāṇapānau vrīhiyavāvanaḍvān prāṇa ucyate /
yave ha prāṇa āhito'pāno vrīhirucyate //13//

[prāṇāpānau vrīhiyavau] prāṇa and apāna are rice and barley. [anaḍvān] ox [prāṇaḥ ucyate] is called the main prāṇa. [yave ha prāṇaḥ āhitaḥ] prāṇa is deposited in barley and [vrīhiḥ apānaḥ ucyate] rice is called apāna.

apānati prāṇati puruṣo garbhe antarā /
yadā tvaṁ prāṇa jinvasyatha sa jāyate punaḥ //14//

[puruṣaḥ garbhe antarā] the embodied soul inside the womb [prāṇati apānati] performs the functions of prāṇa and apāna. O Prāna! when you [jinvasi] impel, motivate, then that [atha saḥ punaḥ jāyate] embodied soul is born again.

prāṇamāhurmātariśvānaṁ vāto ha prāṇa ucyate /
prāṇa ha bhūtaṁ bhavyaṁ ca prāṇe sarvaṁ pratiṣṭhitam //15//

[prāṇaṁ mātariśvānaṁ āhuḥ] prāṇa is called 'mātariśvā' and [vātaḥ ha prāṇah ucyate] air only is called prāṇa. [bhūtam bhavyam sarvam ca ha prāṇe] the past, the future and whatever is there in the present, all of in that 'prāṇa' [pratiṣṭhitam] exists.

ātharvaṇīrāṅgirasīrdaivīrmanuṣyajā utaḥ /
oṣadhayaḥ pra jāyante yadā tvaṁ prāṇa jinvasi //16//

O Prāṇa! [yadā] as long as you [jinvasi] inspire, motivate, [ātharvanīḥ āṅgirasīḥ daivīḥ manuṣyajāḥ oṣadhayaḥ uta] all medicinal plants-ātharvaṇī, daivī and man-made [pra jāyante] bear fruit.

yadā prāṇo abhyavarṣīdvarṣeṇa pṛthivīm mahīm /
oṣadhayaḥ pra jāyante'tho yāḥ kāśca vīrudhaḥ //17//

[yadā prāṇaḥ mahīm pṛthivīm abhyavarṣīt] when prāṅa brings rain on this vast earth, then all [oṣadhayaḥ vīrudhaḥ yāḥ kāḥ ca pra jāyante] the herbs and vegetation, whatever are here, grow and prosper.

yaste prāṇedaṁ veda yasminścāsi pratiṣṭhitaḥ /
sarve tasmai baliṃ harānamuṣmilloka uttame //18//

O Prāṇa! [yaḥ te idam veda] the man who knows this power of yours and [yasmin pratiṣṭhitaḥ asi] the man in whom you are established [tasmai sarve amuṣmin loke balim harān] all offer tributes to him in that supreme sphere.

yathā prāṇa balihṛtastubhyaṁ sarvāḥ prajā imāḥ /
evā tasmai baliṁ harānyastvāṁ śṛṇavat suśravaḥ //19//

O Prāṇa! [yathā] the manner in which [tubhyaṁ sarvāḥ prajāḥ balihṛtaḥ] all people pay you tribute that [yaḥ] anybody who is [su-śravaḥ] of name and fame, and [tvā] pays heed to your power, [tasmai balim harān] offer tributes to him as well.

antargarbhaścaratidevatāsvābhūtobhūtaḥsaujāyatepunaḥ/
sa bhūto bhavyaṁ bhaviṣyatpitā putraṁ pra viveśā śacībhiḥ // 20//

[devatāsu ābhūtaḥ] the prāṇa which exists in sensory organs, etc., the same [antaḥ garbhaḥ carati] moves inside the womb. What [bhūtaḥ] was born in the past, [saḥ] the same [bhavyaṁ bhaviṣyat] is born now and will be born in the future. [pitā] The father [śacībhiḥ] with all this talents [putram pra viveśa] incarnates in his son.

ekaṁ pādaṁ notkhidati salilāddhaṁsa uccaran /
yadaṅga sa samutkhidennaivādya na śvaḥ syānna rātrau nāhaḥ syānna vyucchetkadā cana //21//

[salilāt haṁsaḥ uccaran] the swan rising from the water [ekam pādam na utkhidati] does not raise one leg. [aṅga] O Dear! [yat sa tam utkhidet] if he raises that leg, [na eva adya syāt, na śvaḥ, na rātrīḥ, na ahaḥ syāt, na vyucchet kadā cana] then today, tomorrow, night, day, light and darkness–nothing will happen.

aṣṭācakraṁ vartata ekanemi sahasrākṣaraṁ pra puro ni paścā /
ardhena viśvaṁ bhuvanaṁ jajāna yadasyārdhaṁ katamaḥ sa ketuḥ //22//

[aṣṭācakram] equipped with eight wheels [sahasrākṣaram] having the sahasrākṣara-cakra as its axle and [ekanemi vartate] has only one rim/felly, this type of prāṇa-wheel [pra puraḥ ni paśca] moves back and forth. [ardhena viśvam bhuvanam jajāna] after making all the spheres (lokas) with half portion [yat asya ardham] the half that remains, [katamaḥ saḥ ketuḥ] whose symbol/insignia is this?

yo asya viśvajanmana īśe viśvasya ceṣṭataḥ /
anyeṣu kṣipradhanvane tasmai prāṇa namo'stu te //23//

O Prāṇa! [asya viśva-janmanaḥ] giving birth to all [viśvasya ceṣṭataḥ] of these all who are in motion [yaḥ īśe] who is the lord, [anyeṣu] in all those others [kṣipra-dhanvane namaḥ] one who moves fast, obeisance to thee.

yo asya sarvajanmana īse sarvasya ceṣṭataḥ /
atandro brahmaṇā dhīraḥ prāṇo mā'nu tiṣṭhatu //24//

[yaḥ asya sarvajanmanaḥ] of all taking birth [ceṣṭataḥ sarvasya] of all who move about [īśe] is the lord, that Prāṇa, the very embodiment of patience [atandraḥ] without being lethargic [brahmaṇā dhīraḥ] my prāṇa gaining fortitude from spiritual power [mā] with me [anutiṣṭhatu] always remain.

ūrdhvaḥ supteṣu jāgāra nanu tiryaṅ ni padyate /
na suptamasya supteṣvanu śuśrāva kaścana //25//

[supteṣu] when all have gone to sleep, this prāṇa [ūrdhvaḥ] stands alert [jāgāra] (and) wakes, [nanu tiryaṅ ni padyate] never droops sideways. [supteṣu asya suptam] its going to sleep when all have slept [kaścana na anuśuśrāva] nobody has heard.

prāṇa mā matparyāvṛto na madanyo bhaviṣyasi /
apāṁ garbhamiva jīvase prāṇa badhnāmi tvā mayi //26//

O Prāṇa! [mat mā paryāvṛtaḥ] Don't be separated from me. [na mat anyaḥ bhaviṣyasi] Don't turn your back on me. [apām garbha iva] O Prāṇa, like water, [jīvase mayi tvā badhnāmi] for the purpose of life, I bind you inside me.

THE MEANING OF PRĀNA AND ITS IMPORTANCE

Air (Vāyu), the main element among the five elements, sustains life in our body, and among the three humours (doṣas) it is a doṣa in the form of vāta, and in the form of breath (śvāsa) it is our prāṇa.

pittaṁ paṅgu kaphaḥ paṅguḥ paṅgavo maladhātavaḥ /
vāyunā yatra nīyante tatra gacchanti meghavat //
pavanasteṣu balavān vibhāgakaraṇānmataḥ /
rajoguṇamayaḥ sūkṣmaḥ śīto rūkṣo laghuścalaḥ //

(ŚARṄGADHARA SAṀHITĀ: 5.25-26)

Pitta, kapha, other constituents of the body, mala (waste products) and dhātus (tissues)–they are all cripple, in that they cannot move by themselves in the body from one place to another. It is only air (vāyu) which moves them to different places, much as the wind blows the clouds hither and thither in the sky. Therefore, of the three dosas–vāta, pitta and kapha-vāta wields the power because it separates and distributes all the ingredients, excretions, etc., is full of rajoguṇa (passion, action), is subtle with the ability of penetrating into the tiniest lumens of the whole body, is cold, dry, light in weight and nimble.

Prāṇa has been called Brahman in the Upaniṣads. It permeates every single particle of the body. The motor organs of the body go to sleep, but this pranic energy neither ever sleeps, nor rests. It goes on working, goes on moving day and night; its guiding motto is **'caraiveti, caraiveti'**. The life of all creatures is concurrent with the working of pranic energy. When it stops working in the body, the life of a creature comes to an end. Life exists only till the prāṇas are working; till then a creature is called alive. When the pranic energy stops working, a person is called dead or deceased. Prāṇa is the *sine qua non* of our body.

Prāṇa is the most powerful and useful vital element in the whole universe. Prāṇa is the main prop of life.

It is prāṇa that sustains the body (piṇḍa) and universe (brahmāṇḍa).

The invisible power of prāṇa is running the whole world. Our body is also activated by the energy (elan vital) of prāṇa. Our visible annamaya kośa (physical body) is also activated by the invisible power of our prāṇamaya kośa (etheric body). A person can live for years without food, but without prāṇa life ceases to exist. Prānic energy (aura) is the base of our life-force and immunity. It is prāṇa only which makes the whole body (including the main glands, heart, lungs, brain and spinal cord) healthy and energetic. It is pranic energy that activates vision in eyes, hearing in ears, smelling in nose, relishing in tongue, sweetness in speech, radiance, glow and lustre on face, cognitive power in brain and digestive power in stomach. In the words of Upaniṣad seer :

prāṇasyedaṁ vaśe sarvaṁ tridive yatpratiṣṭhitam /
māteva putrān rakṣava śrīśca prajñāṁ ca vidhehi na iti //

(PRAŚNOPANIṢAD 2.13)

Whatever is there in these three spheres- earth, space and heaven- is controlled by prāṇa. Prāna! Protect us as a mother protects her children with love and affection. Bestow upon us material wealth and mental and spiritual grandeur.

TYPES OF PRĀṈA

Prāṇa is born of Brahman Himself, or from Māyā in the form of matter, Prāṇa is dynamic. The dynamism of this Prāṇa is found in the perennially moving air. In other words prāṇa is that rider who roams about riding on the horse of air. Therefore air (vāyu) is metaphorically called prāṇa. The air in the body is known by different names such as Prāṇa, apāna, etc., based on their location. Pranic energy is one. This Prāṇa is known by various names on the basis of its location and functions. There are main five prāṇas and five upa-prāṇas in the body.

Location of five prāṇas and their functions

1. **Prāṇa (Respiratory system) :** The air that functions in the body from the throat (larynx) to the heart is called 'Prāṇa'.
   Function: This prāṇa activates and energises nasal passage, throat, larynx, tongue, oesophagus, breathing organs, lungs and heart.

2. **Apāna (Excretory system) :** The vital air that moves below the navel (umbilicus) up to mūladhāra cakra is called 'Apāna'.
   Function: Faeces, urine, menstrual blood, semen, flatus and foetus are expelled by this air.

3. **Udāna :** The prāṇa which moves in the region between the larynx and the head is known as 'Udāna'.
   Function: It provides energy to all the organs in the body located in the region above the larynx, viz. eyes, nose, etc. It also lends glow and radiance to the whole face. It activates the whole brain along with the pituitary and pineal glands.

4. **Samāna (Digestive system) :** The prāṇa vāyu which is active in the region between the heart and the navel is called 'Samāna'.
   Function: It controls the internal functioning of the whole digestive system along with liver, intestines, spleen and pancreas.

5. **Vyāna (Circulatory system) :** This vital prānic energy pervades the whole body.

Function: It regulates and controls all activities of the body. It is the vyāna prāṇa which activates and energises the muscles, tissues, joints, pulse and all organs of the body.

Besides these five prāṇas, there are five upa-prāṇas in the body viz., 'devadatta', 'nāga', 'kṛkala, kūrma and 'dhanañjaya' which respectively regulate actions like sneezing, blinking, yawning, seratching the itching skin, hiccupping, etc.

The functioning of prāṇas is linked with prāṇamaya kośa, and prāṇāyāma is mainly responsible for keeping these prāṇas and prāṇamaya kośa clean, healthy and disease-free, hence the highest importance and utility of prāṇāyāma. Before beginning the practice of prāṇāyāma, it is necessary to have a comprehensive knowledge of its background. It is for this reason that the initial chapters of this book are devoted to the explanation of different types of prāṇa and their functions. For easy reference a table on prāṇas is given on the next page.

PRĀṆAS AT A GLANCE

MAIN PRĀṆAS		UPA- PRĀṆAS			
NAME	LOCATION	NAME	LOCATION	CAKRA	ELEMENT
Prāṇa	region around the heart	nāga	a little above the navel	anāhata	air (vāyu)
Apāna	abdomen, anus	kūrma	in the eyelids	mulādhāra	earth (pṛthvi)
Udāna	heart, throat, palate, between the eyebrows and in the brain	devadatta	upper ends of trachea and in the throat	viśuddhi	ether (ākāśa)
Samāna	navel and the region around it	kṛkala	above the stomach and the edges of trachea	maṇipūra	fire (agni)
Vyāna	connected with svādhiṣṭhāna cakra and pervading the whole body	dhanañjaya	in the bones, flesh, skin, blood, receptor sensors, hair, etc.,	svādhiṣṭhāna	water (jala)

THE FIVE SHEATHS (PAÑCAKOŚA) LOCATED IN THE BODY

The human soul is enveloped in five sheaths which are also called five bodies (pañcaśarīra). These five sheaths are described below:

1. **Annamaya kośa (food sheath):** This is the first sheath of the gross body constituted of five elements. The annamaya kośa extends from the skin to the semen, is constituted of seven types of tissues, and is related to the earth (pṛthvī) element. The annamaya kośa remains hale and hearty by regular food and exercise.

2. **Prāṇamaya kośa (vital air sheath):** The second sheath of the body is prāṇamaya kośa. Prāṇa is the medium between the body and the mind. All the work related to performing the cognitive action is done by the prāṇamaya kośa constituted of prāṇa. The prāṇa in the form of inhalation and exhalation is of ten types determined by their location and function, viz, the five main prāṇas: vyāna, udāna, prāṇa, samāna and apāna; and the five upa-praṇas (subordinate prānas): dhanañjaya, nāga, kūrma, kṛkala and devadatta. The main function of prāṇas is to digest the food properly, to gratify the sense organs by a proportionate dispersal and distribution of juices (fluids) in the body, circulating all over in the body along with the blood and throwing out the waste products which mix with the blood in different parts of the body. Consuming various enjoyable things through the body is also its function. The efficiency of prāṇamaya kośa is enhanced by the regular practice of prāṇāyāma.

3. **Manomaya kośa (mind sheath):** This first action-dominated sheath of the subtle body is called manomaya kośa. The manomaya kośa comprises the mind, intellect, ego and psyche, which together form the four–fold inner self (antaḥkaraṇa); and the manomaya kośa is cleansed and strengthened by knowledge and meditation. There are five motor organs which are related more to the affairs of external world.

4. **Vijñānamaya kośa (intellect sheath):** The second sheath of the subtle body dominated by knowledge is called vijñānamaya kośa. Its main components are the intellect empowered by knowledge and the sense organs of perception. The man who conducts himself properly after comprehending the vijñānamaya kośa thoroughly with sagacious perception, and practises dhyāna (meditation) and samādhi (transcendental trance) constantly by detaching himself totally from falsehood, illusion, delusion, attachment, etc., attains ṛtambharā prajñā (pure intellect). The yogi gifted with this intellect restrains his impulsive mind by discernment and non-attachment and attains self-realization.

5. **Ānandamaya kośa (bliss / emotion sheath):** This sheath is also called hiraṇyamaya kośa, hṛdayaguhā, hṛdayākāśa, kāraṇaśarīra, liṅga śarīra, etc. It is located in the region of our heart. It is more affiliated to our inner self, and very little to our outer self. Human life, the existence of the gross body of a human being and all the worldly affairs–all depend on it. On attaining the nirbīja samādhi a sādhaka (seeker) is in a state of perpetual bliss and lives by emancipating himself from the bondage of worldly life.

PRĀṆA- SĀDHANĀ

The main passage of prāṇa is the nose. The inhalation and exhalation through nostrils is the basis of life and prāṇāyāma. The seers and sages invented the prāṇāyāma procedure so that the mind may reveal to the sādhaka the divinity of the inner self hidden deep in the body.

According to Yogadarśana, – **tasmin sati śvāsapraśvāsayorgati-vicchedaḥ prāṇāyāmaḥ** (YOGADARŚANA : 2.49), i.e., on attaining the proper pose (āsana), putting the inhaling-exhaling process in a rhythmic flow is prāṇāyāma. The air which is breathed inside is called śvāsa (inhalation), and the air which is breathed out is called praśvāsa (exhalation). While doing prāṇāyāma, drawing the breath inside is called 'pūraka', holding it inside is 'kumbhaka', and breathing it out is 'recaka'. Holding the breath outside is called 'bahyakumbhaka', and breathing in and holding the breath inside is called 'antaḥkumbhaka'. Thus, puraka, kumbhaka and recaka procedures form part of prāṇāyāma. After perfecting the prāṇāyāma procedures, when it is practised regularly with due care, then according to (YOGADARŚANA : 2.52), **tataḥ kṣīyate prakāśāvaraṇam,** the haze (screen) of ignorance covering the light of knowledge is dispelled, and **dhāraṇāsu ca yogyatā manasaḥ** (YOGADARŚANA : 2.53)–After the prāṇāyāma is perfected the mind becomes capable of attaining dhāranā (concentration), the sixth limb of aṣṭāṅga yoga. In short, I have reached this conclusion that by the practice of prāṇāyāma one attains pratyāhāra (withdrawal), by the constant practice of pratyāhāra one attains dhāraṇā (concentration), by the constant practice of dhāraṇā one attains dhyāna (meditation), and one attains the state of samādhi (transcendental trance) easily by the constant practice of dhyāna. Therefore, I can say on the basis of my experience that prāṇayāma is the very seed of samādhi, or prāṇāyāma culminates into sạmādhi. When the breath enters the body, it is not merely air or oxygen that comes inside, but an indivisible divine energy fills inside which sustains the vitality in the body. Prāṇāyāma is not merely breathing in and breathing out, but one has also to assimilate prāṇic energy or vital force along with air. This vital force permeates everywhere and always, which we may call by any name – God, Iśvara or Khudā, etc. That supreme power is one and the same; and prāṇāyāma is to connect with Him properly; it is the practice of keeping yourself connected.

THE PRĀṆA LORE IN VEDIC LITERATURE

In the assembly of Brahman-devoted learned Brahmins of Pañcāla region, during the splendidly bountiful yajña performed by King Janaka of Videha, the savant Sākalya put this question to Yājñavalkya:

kati devā yājñavalkyaiti?

(BṚHADĀRAṆYAKOPANIṢAD 3.9.1)

Describing respectively three thousand, thirty-three, six, two gods and one god, Yajñavalkya ultimately elaborated upon the manifestation of the greatest one of gods.

katama eko deva iti? prāṇa iti
sa brahma tyadityācakṣate

(BṚHADĀRAṆYAKOPANIṢAD 3.9.9)

"Who is this one god? It is prāṇa. He is also called brahma". Whatever is perishable or imperishable, animate or inanimate in this universe, is the extension of prāṇa brahma. It is prāṇa who is ensconced in the centre, heart or womb of all and is manifesting himself in myriad forms. It is only the yogis and self-realized persons who perceive this prāṇa- origin situated in the navel.

prajāpatiścarati garbhe antarajāyamāno bahudhā vijāyate /
tasya yoniṁ paripaśyanti dhīrāstasmin ha tasthurbhuvanāni
viśvā // (VAJURVEDA 31.19)

In the Śatapatha Brāhmaṇa, prāṇa has been called amṛta (elixir) and prajāpati (creator) :

praṇo amṛtaṁ tad hi agne rūpam(ŚATAPATHA 10.2.6.18)
prāṇo hi prajāpatiḥ (ŚATAPATHA 4.5.5.13)
prāṇo u vai prajāpatiḥ (ŚATAPATHA 8.4.1.4)
prānaḥ prajāpatiḥ (ŚATAPATHA 6.3.1.9)

According to Ayurveda all diseases originate from dyspepsia (mandāgni):

rogāḥ sarve 'pi mande' gnau sutarāmudarāṇi ca /

(AṢṬĀṄGAHṚDAYA NIDĀNASTHĀNA 12)
(MĀDHAVANIDĀNA UDARAROGA 1)

Due to dyspepsia (sluggish digestion) diseases develop in the form of disorder in our seven tissues (dhātus), (three doṣas or humours) and the five constituent elements. According to Ayurveda there are 13 fires–one stomach-fire (jaṭharāgni), five elemental fires (bhūtāgni) and seven tissue fires (dhātvagni), and the treatment of these thirteen fires is called 'kāyacikitsā' in Ayurveda.

kāyasyāntaragneścikitsā kāyacikitsā[1]

(CARAKA SŪTRASTHĀNA 30.28 CAKRAPĀṆI)

Kāyacikitsā is the main medical system of Ayurveda. There are various procedures for the treatment of this fire in Ayurveda. The science of yoga calls this fire by the name of prāṇa. Therefore, if prāṇa therapy, i.e. the treatment of these fires by prāṇāyāma, is administered, it will be the simplest, cheapest, the most authentic and scientific procedure.

prāṇāgnaya evaitasmin pure jāgrati. gārhapatyo ha vā, eṣo'pāno, vyānoless 'nvāhāryapacano yad gārhapatyātpraṇīyate praṇayanādāhavanīyaḥ prāṇaḥ, yaducchvāsaniḥśvāsāvetāvāhutī, samaṁ nayatīti sa samānaḥ, mano ha vāva yajamanaḥ, iṣṭaphalamevodānaḥ sa enaṁ yajamānamaharaharbrahma gamayati. (PRA.U. 4.3)

'In this brahmāgni (i.e. the body) praṇāgnis keep on smouldering (even during the time when the gods [senses, etc] are asleep). Gārhapatya fire is apāna, anvāhārya pacana or dakṣiṇāgni is vyāna, and āhavanīya is prāṇa. The function of samāna is to keep the inhalation–exhalation offerings (śvāsa-praśvasa āhutis) in a balanced state. The mind is the host (yajamāna). The desired fruit is udāna. It takes this mind closer to brahma everyday."

prāṇo vāgniḥ (ŚATAPATHA 2.2.2.15)

tadagnirvai prāṇaḥ

(JAIMINĪYA UPANIṢAD BRĀHMAṆA 4.22.11)

prāṇo agniḥ (ŚATAPATHA 6.3.1.21)

Life is a yajña

puruṣa vai yajñaḥ.

puruṣo vāva yajñaḥ. (ŚATAPATHA 1.3.2.1)

te va ete prāṇā eva yad āhavanīyagārhapatyānvāhāryapaca nākhyā agnayaḥ (ŚATAPATHA 2.2.2.18)

Gārhapatya, dakṣiṇāgni and āhavanīya–these prāṇas are the three fires of this yajña of life. They keep this yajña (life) going. These prāṇas

1. jāṭharaḥ prāṇināmagniḥ kāya ityabhidhīyate–Bhoja / kāyati śabdaṁ karotīti kāyo jāṭharāgniḥ //

(fire) are always active in the yajña of life and they keep this body and sense organs unabatingly aglow, and keep them away from the contact of death.

prāṇāgnaya evaitasmin pure jāgrati (PRAŚNOPANIṢAD 4.3)

Prāṇa itself is Hari -

prāṇo vai hariḥ // (KAUṢĪTAKI BRĀHMAṆA 17.9)

Prāṇa has been called a swan (haṁsa) in Jaiminīya Brāhmaṇa. Riding on this swan (prāṇa) the soul sails across the confines of life and death–**prāṇo vai suparṇaḥ,** i. e. prāṇa itself is suparṇa (haṁsa). Prāṇa and apāna are the celestial physicians of gods who administer their therapy to the whole universe. Death cannot attack in their presence: wherever these godly physicians–prāṇa and apāna–will be present, i.e. whoever practises prāṇāyāma will not die of diseases; he will achieve his full longevity and will conquer death, and will die at will. There is a very interesting and beautiful tale in Brāhmanical texts and purāṇas which, in short, is that Aśvinikumāras, the celestial physicians, rejuvenated the old and decrepit Cyavana Ṛṣi. These prāṇa and apāna themselves are the celestial physicians of gods. Atharvaveda also says.

pratyauhatāmaśvinā mṛtyumasmad devānāmagne bhiṣajā śacībhiḥ (ATHARVAVEDA 7.53.1)

saṁkrāmataṁ mā jahītaṁ śarīraṁ prāṇāpānau te sayujā –viha stām (ATHARVAVEDA 7.53.2)

"O Asvinīkumāras ! Repel Death from us. You are the physicians of gods. We humans may live up to a hundred years."

Whereas the Prāṇa Sūkta of the Atharvaveda describes the immense greatness of pranic energy, the Ṛgveda calls prāṇa the supplier/ provider of medicine, panacea and powers.

ā vāta vāhi bheṣajaṁ vi vāta vāhi yadrapaḥ /
tvaṁ hi viśvabheṣajo devānāṁ dūta īyase //

(ṚGVEDA 10.137.3)

'O Prāṇa! Get to us in the form of medicine, and whatever impurities, contaminants or diseases (rapaḥ) are there, O Vāta, dispel (vi vāhi) them. O Prāṇa, you are the panacea (viśvabheṣaja) as well as the messenger of gods, i,e., you inspire divine sentiments and thoughts.:"

The process of building up health through prāṇyāma is divine therapy. We can achieve complete health and full longevity by balancing through two Aśvinīkumāras (i.e., prāṇa–apāna [anabolism]) the cyavana kriyā (catabolism) in our body. The process of rejuvenating vital fluids in our body is prāṇāyāma. The yoga science was propounded by ancient sages by delving into the secrets of prāṇā vidyā; the same yoga vidyā or prāṇa vidyā will take the pride of place for achieving health, immortality and longevity. The stabilization of prāṇa is immortality; the uprooting of prāṇa is death. Prāṇāyāma is the best way for awakening the serpent power (kuṇḍalinī), for being the one with upward movement of semen (ūrdhvaretā), for uplifting the pranic power, and for preserving the celibacy (brahmacarya).

reto vai prāṇaḥ, prāṇo retaḥ.

Prāṇa itself is semen (reta) or soma rasa. The proper circulation and assimilation of this semen (reta) is celibacy. It is supreme penance. With the perfect cooking / nurturing of this brahma rice (brahmaudana), immortality in the body is generated. This is what we call 'soma- pāna' (drinking the elixir of life).

yasmātpakvādamṛtaṁ saṁbabhūva
yo gāyatryā adhi patirbabhūva /
yasmin vedā nihitā viśvarūpās
tenaudanenātitarāṇi mṛtyum // (ATHARVAVEDA 4.35.6)

'With that brahmaudana, the perfect cooking / assimilation of which in the body generates the elixir of life (amṛtatva) which is lord of celibacy (gāyatrī) which holds the vedas epitomizing the whole universe, with that perfectly cooked rice (reta- vital fluid/ semen) I transcend Death."

In the Vedic lore, brahmāṇḍa or cerebrum is the heaven. The abode of the sensory power (indriya-śakti) of Indra is brahmāṇḍa (cerebrum). The centres of all the sense organs are located here wherefrom Indra regulates prāṇas. Prāṇa is the force behind all external sensory and motor functions. As their regulator, Indra is the lord of brahmāṇḍa (cerebrum) or heaven. That Indra enjoys immortality by drinking soma. What is this soma?

Some people say that 'soma' is a vegetation of nature or a creeper, and go on fantasizing about it. To limit the meaning of soma to a mere creeper is to cripple the wider meaning of soma. Physically soma may be a creeper, but in the purely Vedic lore soma has a very comprehensive meaning. Soma is the name of all creepers, vegetation and foodgrains. According to Śatapatha, foodgrain (anna) is soma:

annaṁ vai somaḥ. (Śat. 2.9.18)

The energy generated by consuming this anna is also soma. Satapatha, Kauṣītaki and Tāṇdya Brāhrnaṇas, etc. say that soma is the name of prāṇa. After eating the food, the subtle electricity–like energy generated in the body by the transformation of its gross part is called prāṇa, which is soma itself. And also the purest form of energy and the very extract secreted from all the tissues, which is semen or reta, that too is soma. Therefore the authors of Brāhmaṇas say:

reto vai somaḥ **(Śat. 1.9.2.6)**

There is none more divine substance to energise the brahmāṇḍa (cerebrum) than this soma or reta (semen). Semen (reta) is the transformed state of water. The water on earth evaporates into space by the heat of the sun. Similarly the water (fluid energy) staying in the svādhiṣṭhana cakra ascends to the bratmāṇḍa (cerebrum) or heaven through austere penance. After its ascent to heaven (cerebrum), the soma or reta (semen) propels and gratifies the prāṇas and sense organs in the whole body. This soma is the most favourite drink of Indra (manaś-cakra). It is also called amṛta (elixir). The preservation of soma (semen) gives a person immortality; wasting it away leads to death. An increase in the properties (katās) of soma results in the increase of elixir. With the waning of those properties the mental centre (manaścakra) tends to decline. This spiritual fact is denoted in the myth of the waning and waxing of moon. Gods nurture their soma; demons (asuras) drink it away. That part of life on which the soma increases is bright fortnight (śukla pakṣa), and the part when the soma is on the decline is the dark fortnight (kṛṣṇa pakṣa). These two phases constitute not only the human life, but also the whole nature. Sometimes there is rise, sometimes fall. This applies to all the creatures, animals, vegetation, immortality and mortality. The increase and decrease of soma in the vegetation follows the laws of nature, but the human being violates the nature in many ways. He is a conscious and cognisant being. Realizing the soma as the chief energizer of life the sages have preached in many ways for its preservation and cultivation. The cultivation / nurturing of soma leads to successful celibacy. In fact, celibacy (brahmacarya) is indispensable for the realization of soul. "If a man believes in the entity of soul and at the same time indulges in vice, he seems to accept the existence of darkness in the presence of the sun." (MAHATMA GANDHI). Sages and seers, dwellers of hermitages and āśramas in forests, have declared about spiritualism :

satyena labhyastapasā hyeṣa ātmā
samyagjñānena brahmacaryeṇa nityam. **(MU. UP.3.5)**

'This soul (ātmā) can be realized only through truth, austere penance, proper knowledge and constant celibacy.'

The great sages who in the hoary past resolved through meditation (dhyāna yoga) that all the beings be blessed and happy also resorted to austere training and penance. Only then the kingdom, force, radiance, etc. came into existence.

bhadramicchanta ṛṣayaḥ svarvidastapo
dīkṣāmupaniṣeduragre /
tato rāṣṭra balamojaśca jātaṁ tadasmai
devā upasaṁnamantu // **(ATHARVA. 19.41.1)**

Besides these āśrama- dwelling sages, there are seven ṛṣis in the body too. These seven ṛṣis are the seven most important prāṇas. Bṛhadāraṇyaka Upaniṣad says:

prāṇā vā ṛṣayaḥ / **(BR.U.2.2.3)**

The seven prāṇas are the seven ṛṣis whose names are as follows: Gautama, Bhāradvāja–two ears; Viśvāmitra, Jamadagni–two eyes; Vasiṣṭha, Kaśyapa–two nostrils; Atri–speech. These seven ṛṣis are the knowers of svaḥ, i.e. heaven, cerebrum or higher brain. First of all they practise austere penance. Since birth the senses are inclined toward initiation into penance. Their impulses are chaste and controlled like ṛṣis. Only then radiance (oja) comes and kingdom (rāṣṭra) is born- the body as a kingdom in which the subjects are not rebellious and they inhabit there by accepting the soul as their sovereign. On growing up, the senses start getting out of control, which gives rise to a rebellion in the kingdom. With a view to bringing coordination among them, the seven ṛṣis resorted to their voluntary initiation into austere penance (tapas). It is from tapas that the kingdoms (raṣtras) develop; profligacy brings about their downfall. It may be the kingdom of our body, or on the wider plane the kingdom of a country, penance/ discipline should be inculcated in every individual,– this is what the mantra quoted above purports to say. Thus, preserving the vital fluid (vīrya- semen) in the first stage of life through methodically performed penance and celibacy is a great triumph and accomplishment of a man's life. This is the basic code which if properly complied with can make one's life a success. One does not get this opportunity many times. If one commits a blunder in the first stage (āśrama) it cannot be rectified. The vast compendium of Aryan scriptures contains many rules and procedures for the successful preservation of celibacy in the first stage of life. It is from this seed (semen) that all physical, mental, spiritual, social and national progress and development take root. How striking is this line from Kumārasaṁbhavam where Siva disguised as a brahmacārī says to Parvatī who is performing austere penance:

mamāpi pūrvāśramasañcitaṁ tapaḥ

'I too have got the tapa accumulated in the first stage of my life. O Parvati, if you like you may accomplish your desires by its power." This tapa is to be done by the senses voluntarily. The mantra points to this general rule. With the desire of common good the ṛṣis initiated themselves into austere penance. It is very difficult to initiate oneself into tapa by external restraint of sense organs alone. It one tries to achieve such control and restraint, it results in a very dangerous wantonness.

Thus, the soma - drinking of Indra encapsulates the mystery of the Indian Brahmacarya lore. The secret of digesting / assimilating the energy of body within the body itself can be named as soma-pāna. This generates amazing ecstasy and courage in a person which propels him to declare : **hantāhaṁ pṛthivīmimāṁ nidadhānīha veha vā. kuvit somasyāpāmiti.** (ṚGVEDA 10.119.9). There are various types of this energy. The gross physical soma is śukra (semen), the glow or radiance (dyumna, teja) of which illumines every pore of our body. The radiance which is born when retas is burnt to ashes is called bhasma. It is necessary for everybody to get smeared all over by this type of bhasma. Siva is the supreme yogi. To become an akhaṇḍa ūrdhvaretā (one who has an upward movement of semen perenially), he has burnt kāma (Cupid, sexual desire) to ashes. Therefore none else has the radiant body like him glowing with the radiant bhasma. The brahmāṇda (cerebrum) in everybody is the Kailāsa where Siva resides. If this Siva–like energy of the brain is properly addressed in such a way that it becomes totally devoid of sexual desire, one can achieve the same results as Indra achieved by drinking the soma. One and the same Maharṣi element has been described in two contexts. By burning Kāma to ashes Siva stores the energy of the six cakras in his body. Indra (or the Lord Protector of prāṇas seated in the cerebrum) enhances immortality by imbibing the semen (retas) of body or soma. To the scholars having a comprehensive knowledge of Vedic lore it is quite easy to understand the relation between such hypotheses. Kauṣītaki Brāhmaṇopaniṣad says that the great sage Kauṣītaki has declared the same thing in an assembly of seers-

"prāṇo brahma' iti ha smāha kauṣītakiḥ" (KAU. U. 2.1)

Similarly the sage Paiṅgya, on the basis of his experience gained through austere penance, propounded this truth in the words:

"prāṇo brahma' iti ha smāha paiṅgyaḥ. (KAU. U. 2.2)

All Upaniṣads, Brāhmaṇas, Āraṇyakas and Saṁhitās sing the glory of prāṇa. Prāṇa resides in all in the form of longevity / life span (āyu). With the uprooting of prāṇa, the life span is cut short and collapses. Prāṇa is the best, oldest and seniormost of all the gods. With the stabilization of prāṇa all other gods come and settle in this Brahmapurī. Prāṇa is the stabilizer of the boat of this body :

prāṇo vai suśarmā supratiṣṭhānaḥ (ŚAT 4.4.1.14)

and -

prāṇa eṣa sa puri śete. (GOPATHA. PŪ. 1.39)

"On account of residing in the city of body it is prāṇa itself which is called puruṣa". Prāṇa manifests itself in the forms of Vasu, Rudra and Āditya. One of the names of prāṇa is 'arka' :

prāṇo vā arkaḥ (ŚAT. 10.4.1.23)

It is prāṇa that makes this gross body adorable. The moment prāṇa leaves it we start despising it, and it is discarded. That is why prāṇa is called 'arka'. Prāṇa itself is elixir (amṛta).

amṛtamu vai prāṇaḥ. (ŚAT. 9.1.2.32)

It is prāṇa that imparts immortality to this mortal body. This is what Indra said to Pratardana:

prāṇo'smi prajñātmā. taṁ māmāyuramṛtamityupāssvā 'yuḥ prāṇah prāṇo vā āyuḥ yāvadasmiñcharīre prāṇo vasati tāvadāyuḥ. Prāṇena hi evāsmin loke' mṛtatvamāpnoti.

(ŚĀṄKHĀYANA ĀRAṆYAKA 5.2)

'I am intelligence in the form of prāṇa. Know me as life- span and elixir, and worship me. The life–span is concurrent with the existence of prāṇa. Immortality in the world is attained only through prāṇa. The sentient power that props up this mortal frame i.e., due to which circulation of energy is seen, is prāṇa only."

prāṇa eva prajñātmā.
idaṁ śarīraṁ parigṛhya utthāpayati.
–yo vai prāṇaḥ sā prajñā, yā vā prajñā
sa prāṇaḥ. **(KAUṢĪTAKI 3.3)**

Whatever intelligence exists in the universe or in the body is prāṇa. From a mosquito to Brahman–all sentient beings are charged with the energy of prāṇa.

Prāṇa is the symbol (liṅga) or phallus (śepa) of that sentient power (cit-śakti). The symbol in the form of prāṇa appears to be that supreme consciousness. That is why prāṇa is also named as Śunaḥśepa. Aśva (horse) and Śvāna (dog) are also the names of prāṇa, In fact, in the Vedic lore, all animate beings denote prāṇa. Puruṣa (man), go (cow, bull), aśva (horse), ajā (goat), avi (sheep) – they are all specific names of prāṇa. From a trivial ant to the greatest wonder of nature, i.e. the man, all are the symbols of dog like prāṇa. According to Brāhmaṇa scriptures, prāṇa is soma, prāṇa is agni. praṇa is Mitra, prāṇa is Varuṇa. In the Maitrāvaruṇa mantras the glory or secrets of prāṇa - apāna have been described. Prāṇa is a god, Prāṇa is Bālakhilya, because in the continuity or extension of prāṇas there is not even a hair–breadth gap.

bālamātrādu heme prāṇā asaṁbhinnāste yad
bālamātrādasambhinnāstasmād bālakhilyāḥ. (ŚAT. 8.3.4.1)

Prāṇa itself is ṛk, yaju and sāma. The rays of light are prāṇa.

sahasraraśmiḥ śatadhā vartamānaḥ
prāṇaḥ prajānāmudayatyeṣa sūryaḥ. **(ŚAT. 6.7.120)**
(PRA. UP. 1.8)

Prāṇa is the year. Prāṇa is the truth. Prāṇa is a big heavy container (śikya) hanging from the ceiling and everything is tied up in it.

The ṛṣi poses the question: Who does not sleep in this Brahmapurī?

tadāhuḥ ko'svaptumarhati, yadvāva prāṇo jāgāra tadeva
jāgaritam iti. **(TĀṆḌYA 10.4.4)**

The awakening of prāṇa is the great awakening. The great sage Pippalāda says in Praśnopaniṣad–

prāṇāgnaya evāsmin brahmapure jāgrati.

"The fires of prāṇa are perennially ablaze (awake) in the Brahmanagarī of this body."

There is a mantra in Yajurveda:

sapta ṛṣayaḥ pratihitāḥ śarīre
sapta rakṣanti sadamapramādam /
saptāpaḥ svapato lokamīyustatra
jāgṛto asvapnajau satrasadau ca devau // **(YAJU 34.35)**

Almost all the commentators have interpreted this mantra as referring to prāṇa. Even Griffith has similar comments.

sapta ṛṣayaḥ	=	seven prāṇas
sapta āpaḥ	=	seven prāṇas or sense organs
two awakened gods	=	prāṇa and apāna

"Seven ṛṣis dwell in this body. The seven ever - watchful sentinels defend it vigilantly. The seven out- flowing prāṇa - streams or sense organs retire into the dream - world of the sleeper. At that time too the two ever - wakeful gods (prāṇa and apāna) keep company with the ever–vigilant soul."

Prāṇa and Ṛṣi

Ṛṣi is also a name for prāṇa.

prāṇa vā ṛṣayaḥ.
imaveva gotamabharadvājau.
ayameva gotamaḥ, ayaṁ bharadvājaḥ.
imaveva viśvāmitrajamadagnī.
ayameva viśvāmitraḥ, ayaṁ jamadagniḥ.
imaveva vasiṣṭhakaśyapau.
ayameva vasiṣṭhaḥ, ayaṁ kaśyapaḥ.
vāgevātriḥ. **(BṚHAD. U. 2.2.4)**

'The seven ṛṣis are the seven prāṇas. The two ears are Gautama and Bhāradvāja. The two eyes are Viśvāmitra and Jamadagni. The two nostrils are Vasiṣṭha and Kaśyapa. The speech is Atri."

This head is the abode of gods (devakośa), which is also called heavenly sphere.

tadvā atharvaṇaḥ śiro devakośaḥ samubjitaḥ /
tatprāṇo abhi rakṣati śiro annamatho manaḥ //

'This head is a well- closed chest or box of gods. Prāṇa, mind and anna (or speech= gross body) defend it."

It is a marvel of Nature that the seven ṛṣis of human body dwell in this devakośa or heaven i.e. the head. The seven passages or holes in the head illumine like the seven ṛṣis (saptarṣi). It is the head that is the centre of luminosity or consciousness in the body. The five sense organs of perception are also there. Knowledge or light is the luminosity of gods. The various centres of perception / knowledge are the various gods. The abode of all these gods is the heaven called head. Similarly, the abode of the seven sages (saptarṣi) called the prāṇas is the brain (cerebrum). Bṛhadāranyaka Upaniṣad elaborates upon it:

arvāgbilaścamasa ūrdhvabudhnas-
tasminyaśo nihitaṁ viśvarūpam /
tasyāsata ṛṣayaḥ sapta tire
vāgaṣṭamī brahmaṇā saṁvidānā //

This has also been explained in the Upaniṣads. 'This head is a bowl with its bottom upward and its mouth downward. The seven sages (saptarṣi) dwell on its margins. Speech in dialogue with Brahman is the eighth one."

In short, as the saptarṣi constellation shines in the sky (heavens)' so do the seven prāṇas named after seven ṛṣis illumine the heaven of cerebrum.

Maharṣi Pippatāda sings the great glory of prāṇa in Praśnopaniṣad (2):

arā iva rathanābhau prāṇe sarvaṁ pratiṣṭhitam /
ṛco yajūṁṣi sāmāni yajñaḥ kṣatraṁ brahma ca //
prajāpatiścarasi garbhe tvameva pratijāyase /
tubhyaṁ prāṇa prajāstvimā baliṁ haranti yaḥ prāṇaiḥ pratitiṣṭhasi //
devānāmasi vahnitamaḥ pitṛṇāṁ prathamā svadhā /
ṛṣīṇāṁ caritaṁ satyamatharvāṅgirasāmasi //
indrasvaṁ prāṇa tejasā rudro'si parirakṣitā /
tvamantarikṣe carasi sūryastvaṁ jyotiṣāṁ patiḥ //
yadā tvamabhivarṣasyathemāḥ prāṇa te prajāḥ /
ānandarūpāstiṣṭhanti kāmāyānnaṁ bhaviṣyatīti //
vrātyastvaṁ prāṇaikarṣirattā viśvasya satpatiḥ /
vayamādyasya dātāraḥ pitā tvaṁ mātariśva naḥ //
yā te tanūrvāci pratiṣṭhitā yā śrotre yā ca cakṣuṣi /
yā ca manasi santatā śivāṁ tāṁ kuru motkramīḥ //
prāṇasyedaṁ vaśe sarvaṁ tridive yatpratiṣṭhitam /
māteva putrān rakṣasva śrīśca prajñāṁ vidhehi na iti //

"As there are rods fixed to the axle of the chariot, similarly ṛk, yaju, sāma, yajña and all kṣatriyas and brāhmaṇas, etc., eligible to perform yajña, are established in prāṇa.

"O Prāṇa, you move in the womb in the form of Prajāpati. You take birth in various forms. O Prāṇa, since you reside in different parts of the body along with sense organs (prāṇas) like eyes, etc., therefore all the people make their offerings to you.

'You are the carrier of the best havi for gods. The oblations of food offered to the prāṇa–fire of the body reach the gods (i.e. sense organs) only through you, and you are the first and foremost food of manes. You are the righteous conduct of Atharvāṇgiras ṛṣis who initiated the yajña rituals by kneading (kindling) the fire. (The divine activities of prāṇa, are the righteous rituals of yajña.)

'O prāṇa, by your bright lustre (which distinguishes one thing from another) you are Indra. You are the preserver (Viṣṇu). You are the air permeating the space. You are the sun, the lord of luminous stars.

"O Prāṇa! When you (as a cloud) bring rain, then these subjects of yours rejoice that now there will be plenty of food (a rich harvest)."

'O Prāṇa, you are vrātya (raw, unrefined), i.e. you are beyond rituals and refinements, because you are purity itself. You are a seer. You are a consumer of anna (Soma is your anna). You are the lord of the universe. We all offer anna. You are the one wandering in the space (mātariśva). You are our father.

'O Prāṇa, make that form of yours good and noble (śiva) which inhabits our speech, ears, eyes and mind. Please, never let it take off (get uprooted) from our body.

'Whatever is there in the three spheres of universe is under the control of prāṇa. O Prāṇa, protect us as a mother protects her children and bless us with prosperity and intelligence."

prāṇāya namo yasya sarvamidaṁ vaśe. (ATHARVA. 11.4.1)

'I salute Prāṇa. All this universe is under the control of Prāṇa."

This paean to Prāṇa harks back to that holy past when the ṛṣis and brahmacārīs in hermitages knew the secrets of the prāṇic lore and achieved mental trance, complete health and full longevity by disciplining the prāṇas.

This mantra saya 'O Prāṇa, protect us like Mother Universe. We are your children "The sages of yore lost all worries after entrusting their disciples to the arms of mother-like prana, and those disciples drank the propitious honey or milk like elixir of that universe–feeding mother and attained immortality and holy radiance. The eternal (sanātana) yogavidyā (yogic lore) is another name for prāṇavidyā (prāṇic lore). The knowledge of the secrets of prāṇa is samprāpti. Whatever is there inside or outside this universe is encompassed by prāṇa.

Prāṇa is all–devouring, all–absorbing (saṁvarga)[1] :

> **prāṇo vāva saṁvargaḥ. sa yadā svapiti prāṇameva vāgapyeti prāṇaṁ cakṣuḥ prāṇaṁ śrotraṁ prāṇaṁ manaḥ prāṇo hyevaitān sarvān saṁvṛṅkta iti.(CHA. UP. 4.3.3)**

Prāṇa is all–devouring. When he (the puruṣa) sleeps, then the speech is merged in Prāṇa. It is only in Prāṇa where the eyes, ears and mind are merged, because Prāṇa devours them all.

> **tau vā etau dvau saṁvargau vāyureva deveṣu prāṇah prāpeṣu.**

There are definitely those two devourers–it is the air (Vāyu) among gods, and the Prāṇa among sense organs like speech, etc.

Three spheres :

> **vāgevāyaṁ lokaḥ mano'ntarikṣalokaḥ prāṇo'sau lokaḥ.**

"Speech is the sphere of earth, mind is the sphere of space, and prāṇa is the sphere of heaven." Therefore, one ascends to heaven with the practice of prāṇāyāma. A sphere full of all sorts of comfort and happiness is heaven itself.

Bird –

> **sa yathā sakuniḥ sūtreṇa prabaddho, diśaṁ diśaṁ patitvā, anyatrāyatanamalabdhvā, bandhanamevopaśrayate, evameva khalu saumya tanmano diśaṁ diśaṁ patitva, anyatrāyatanamalabdhvā, prāṇamevopaśrayate, prāṇabandhanaṁ hi saumya mana iti. (CHA. UP. 6.8.2)**

"As a bird tied to a string, having strayed from one quarter to another, and not finding shelter in any place, comes back to its starting point; similarly, dear disciple, this mind roams and strays into many quarters, and not finding shelter in any other place, resorts to prāṇa only, because, dear disciple, the mind is tied to prāṇa only."

Thus, the mind has an association with prāṇa. That is why with the strengening of prāṇa through prāṇayāma the mind also becomes strong. If the prāṇa is unstable, the mind becomes fickle. With the stability of prāṇa, the mind also becomes stable. Due to the restraining of mind through prāṇa other sense organs also are independent of the restraint of prāṇa.

---

1. sarveṣaṁ sangrahītā grasayita

YOGA - A PHILOSOPHY OF LIFE

Yoga is a philosophy of life. Yoga is a self–discipline. Yoga is a life–style. Yoga is a concept of life, free of diseases and rich with transcendental trance. Yoga is an excellent spiritual lore of self-therapy and self–realization. Through this spiritual science of yoga, a pygmy can become a colossus or one can transform or develop oneself comprehensively. Yoga is not merely an alternative system of medicine; its authenticity is based on the results of experiments which show that the diseases have been eradicated. It is therefore a complete system of medicine, not only for diseases of the body but also for those of the mind.

Yoga is not a symptomatic medical treatment like allopathy, rather it makes us feel healthy from inside by eradicating the root cause of diseases. To view yoga merely as a form of exercise or merely as a ritualistic system of a particular community is a narrow and foolish attitude. We should view yoga as a complete science, throwing aside selfishness, prejudice, ignorance and egoism.

The scriptures say that the eight cakras (energy centres) are awakened by yoga, and by the constant practice of prāṇāyāma the sins and evil impressions accumulated over several births get destroyed.

When we probed into the scientific background of eight cakras and compared the ancient scriptural terms with the modern medical science we found that the mūlādhāra, svādhiṣṭhāna, maṇipūra, hṛdaya, anāhata, ājñā and sahasrāra cakras correspond respectively to the reproductory, excretory, digestive, skeletal, circulatory, respiratory, nervous and endocrine systems. The function of the eight cakras from mūlādhāra to sahasrāra is similar to the function of reproductory to endocrine systems. The eight prāṇāyāmas of kriyātmaka yoga keep these eight cakras or eight systems activated and balanced.

The imbalance of even a single system causes diseases and disorders of various types. In spite of the difference of languages, the sense behind spiritualism and science is one and the same. Language is merely a medium of expressing feelings and thoughts. A long period of four centuries of slavery and self–degradation created a psyche in which anabolism, catabolism and metabolism found an easier access than vāta, pitta and kapha.

It was only our ignorance that instead of feeling proud of our tradition, culture and knowledge, we lapsed into self- degradation. The word 'cakra' puzzled us, but with the word 'system' we developed so much familiarity and affinity that we started calling ourselves systematic, while the purpose behind the quest for knowledge in the ancient as well as in the modern times was the same–realization of truth.

Instead of the Ayurvedic principle: **prajñāparādho hi sarvarogā ṇāṁ mūlakāraṇaṁ**[1] (CARAKA), we started feeling it more scientific to say: 'stress is the main cause of all diseases'. Now is the time to give up prejudice and ignorance, and to adopt the truth. For example, the imbalance of endocrine system causes stress which, in turn, causes a number of complicated diseases like heart disease, hypertension, depression, obesity and diabetes, Similarly, the imbalance in skeletal system causes arthritis (of more than a hundred types) and a person falls prey to a host of muscular disorders. In short, any imbalance in the internal system is disease, while a balanced internal system means a healthy body.

With the direct and indirect experiments of yoga on millions of people we have found that by practising mainly eight prāṇāyāmas properly for a definite period with determination all our eight cakras or eight systems get fully balanced. As a result we enjoy a healthy life with yoga. At the same time, we gradually dispense with the necessity of taking externally the chemical salts or hormones in the form of medicine, because all those chemical salts and hormones we start getting internally in a balanced quantity.

Instead of being a pigeon–hole treatment like allopathy, yoga is a complete concept of health. Barring emergency medicine or surgical treatment, yoga is the best form of therapy covering all other areas

---

1. Compare :

buddhyā viṣamavijñāṁ viṣamaṁ ca pravartanam/
prajñaparādhaṁ jānīyān manaso gocaraṁ hi tat //

(CA. ŚĀRĪRASTHĀNA 1.109)

dhīdhṛtismṛtivibhṛṣṭaḥ karma yat kurute'shubham /
prajñāparādhaṁ taṁ vidyāt sarvadoṣaprakopanam //

(CA. ŚĀRĪRA. 1.102)

of medicine. In some complicated ailments, if yoga is combined with Ayurveda, the treatment becomes extremely effective.

Along with this health aspect, the spiritual aspect of yoga is immensely vast. Though the main aim of yoga is the attainment of samadhi (transcendental trance) or the attainment of svarūpa (self–realisation) or the realisation of the Supreme Truth, yet in this journey of attaining samādhi through yoga the hurdles (diseases) in the way are removed automatically, which means that the elimination of disease through yoga is only a bye-product of yoga. We should never forget that the main aim is samādhi. These thoughts on yoga are not merely intellectual acrobatics, or a dream, blandishments or assurances; they are the reality of the experiments of yoga. I am fully assured that in the days ahead the whole world will shed away its prejudices and will adopt yoga in a big way, and yoga will help build a peaceful, healthy, sensitive and prosperous nation and world. There will be complete development with the co-ordination of science and spirituality, materialism and spiritualism. Yoga will awaken a sense of duty toward self as well as the nation. The world will march forward on the path of welfare of self as well as of the whole world. An individual will emancipate himself from the surrounding confusion of many 'isms', such as casteism, communalism, provincialism, linguism, Marxism, Maoism and Manu-ism, etc., and will adopt nationalism and humanitarianism, and India will establish herself as the supreme cultural, spiritual, economic and social power of the world. The agitated mind is the breeding ground of fear, hatred, greed, discontent, ignorance, anger, lack of restraint and all negative thoughts. When the mind of a person will become calm through prāṇāyāma and meditation, the fear, illusion, violence, crime and corruption rampant in the society, nation and world will also disappear, and with the inclination toward worship the indulgence into desires will also be controlled. The only solution to emancipation from epicurean extremes is this yogic way of life. If we want to put an end to this formidable age of the globalisation of violence, crime and lasciviousness, it is possible only by propagating yoga on a world–wide scale, otherwise nobody can save us from total havoc and perdition.

THE TWO PRINCIPLES OF MEDICINE

Whereas the symptomatic and the systemic treatments form the pillars of the medical science based on modem medical systems, Yoga and Ayurveda is a science of eradicating all diseases by bringing about a balance in the system. Barring malaria, tuberculosis, etc., medicine is administered in allopathy to maintain the disorders and diseases like hypertension, diabetes, asthma and thyroid, etc. There is no permanent cure of these diseases in allopathy whereas diseases like B.P., thyroid and asthma are cured through yoga and natural life– style. It we divide prāṇāyāma in two parts : 1. pre-anuloma-viloma, and 2. post-anuloma - viloma, in the first part the bhastrikā, kapālabhāti and bāhya- prāṇāyāma procedures make our reproductory, excretory, digestive and skeletal systems comprehensively healthy and balanced, and in the second part the anuloma - viloma, bhrāmarī, udgītha and praṇava prāṇāyāmas endow us with complete health by fully balancing our circulatory, respiratory, nervous and endocrine systems. Many people are sceptic about it that in allopathy there are different medicines for different diseases, then how can all the diseases be cured simultaneously through yoga by practising mainly eight prāṇāyāmas and a few yogic procedures? It is quite natural for a common man to have this doubt in his mind: why should there be same yoga for people having different ailments? To resolve this doubt we have to understand physiology and psychology properly and also do a scientific analysis of the effects of procedures of yogic science.

All of us may have different bodies, but in spite of having distinct bodies and minds, the internal system of our bodies, our endocrine glands, our reproduetory organs, our physical body right from mūlādhāra cakra to sahasrāra or brahmarandhra and our etheric body formed of the mind, intellect, psyche and ego, etc, are one and the same. All of us have the three doṣas–vāta , pitta and kapha in the texture of our body. The mind of all of us is constituted of three guṇas (qualities)– sattva (goodness, purity), rajas (passion, activity) and tamas (inertia, ignorance). There is very subtle distinction between men only at the level of D.N.A. and impressions (saṁskāras). The difference at D.N.A. level is meant to give a distinct identity to each individual, and the difference at the level of impressions is on the basis of deeds and knowledge accumulated by us in this birth and previous births. This difference at both the levels is only to give us all on independent identity.

In the field of medicine this difference has no significance. In the modern medical science the norms set for a healthy person, be they various tests of blood or the tests related to hormones, heart, liver, kidneys or brain, the testing procedure for all is the same. For example, the procedure for measuring blood pressure, sugar, cholesterol, etc., or the procedure for angiography, C.T. scan, M.R.I., ultrasound, x–ray and endoscopy and their norms are the same for all individuals. On empty stomach the blood sugar level in each case should be below 100 and the cholesterol level below 150. The shape and size, weight and functioning of the liver, kidneys and heart of all persons should be the same, then why not the same yoga for all. One and the same yoga is there to correct the one and the same system of all individuals. It is there to balance the three doṣas–vāta, pitta and kapha. Just as in Ayurveda there are different medicines for different doṣas–vata, pitta and kapha, but a few medicines like giloya (tinospora cordifolia) etc., pacify all the three doṣas, similarly yoga and prāṇāyāma pacify all the three doṣas and they take us beyond the three guṇas, sattva-rajas-tamas, into a guṇātīta (guṇa-inapplicable) state. As the great sage Patañjali himself says: **puruṣārthaśūnyānāṁ guṇānāṁ pratiprasvaḥ kaivalyaṁ svarūpapratiṣṭhā vā citi śaktiriti (KAI. PĀ. 4.34).** Yoga takes us to the portals of consciousness beyond the mind: **"yogaścitlavṛttinirodhaḥ" (SA. PĀ. 1.2).** Yoga emancipates us from the accumulated impressions / dispositions of this birth as well as previous births and makes us realize our real self. Therefore, yoga is the same for all individuals because in spite of being distinct identities we are essentially one and the same.

Impacting our system, mind, doṣas and saṁskāras simultaneously and uniformly, yoga makes every individual completely healthy physically as well as mentally, which ultimately helps him being situated in the self, while allopathic medicines work on the system and are of different types due to their being based on the system. This is the basic difference between yoga and allopathy.

In allopathy an attempt is made to balance the chemicals, etc, inside the patient by administering and injecting medicines, chemical salts or hormones from outside, while through the practice of prāṇāyama, etc. We produce the chemical salts and hormones, etc. from inside by maintaining the balance internally. After comprehending this science this ignorance is dispelled as to how one yoga can cure many diseases simultaneously. Almost the same principle applies to Ayurveda as in the case of yoga. Like yoga, the medicinal herbs of Ayurveda and its other medical procedures work on our eight systems and balance the internal system. For example, as the Caraka Saṁhitā says, śilājīta is efficacious in all the diseases.

na so'sti rogo bhuvi sādhyarūpaḥ
śilāhvayaṁ yaṁ na jayet[1] prasahya **(CARAKA)**

"There is no disease in the world which cannot be cured by śilājīta," because śilajīta has a direct effect on our reproductory system to respiratory system. That means it increases the sperm count and cures other sexual disorders. Disorders of urinary system are cured. Śilājīta is also efficacious in curing the disorders of liver and pancreas by balancing the digestive system. By strengthening bones and muscles it brings into order the skeletal system and circulatory system and completely rectifies the locomotion of the body. Śilajīta cures all the diseases of respiratory system by giving energy to lungs. When these six systems work properly, our autonomic and nervous system is also well controlled. Similarly, when the whole internal system of the body is balanced, our endocrine glands are well- regulated. Thus, śilājīta gives health and energy to all the eight systems indirectly. Therefore, śilājīta alone is the panacea for all diseases. Like śilajīta there are other Ayurvedic medicines and herbs which singly cure many diseases. It is not so in allopathy. There is a separate medicine for each disease because that medicine covers a few symptoms and does not cover the whole system. Therefore, one allopathic medicine does not cover many diseases. In yoga and Ayurveda, instead of treating the symptoms, we treat the cause. We rectify the base, i.e., we make healthy and energetic the eight cakras from mūlādhāra to sahasrāra or the eight systems. This is where our ancient traditional medicine and the modern medicine differ in principle. The very philosophy and approach of the two systems of medicine differs from each other. Therefore, if we have to overcome the differences between

---

1. Āyurvedaprakāśa Śrīmadmādhava Upādhyāya (A. 4.128)

the medical systems, we have to rise above ignorance, prejudice, selfishness and ego and understand properly the principles of both the systems of medicine, and will have to accept that medical system without any prejudice which is beneficial for the ailing mankind. Allopathic treatment is excellent in life-saving procedures, surgery, emergency, tuberculosis, malaria, etc,. and also in the diagnosis of diseases the modern system of medicine has done an excellent job. On the other hand, by regulating properly the system of the body with the help of yoga and Ayurveda, we can get rid completely of the chronic ailments like asthma, hypertension, arthritis, depression, migraine pain and diseases of the liver, kidneys, intestines and heart, etc. Therefore we should definitely come forward to make use of yoga and Ayurveda for the welfare of the whole world. A patient's welfare is the topmost priority. A patient's welfare should be given priority over our individual commercial interests.

THE SELF- TRIED TRUTH OF PRĀṆĀYĀMA

1. From the age of 3 years children can practise prāṇāyāma and sūkṣma vyāyāmas (light exercises) and even the aged must practise prāṇāyāma until their last breath. Children should start doing āsanas at the age of 5 years.
2. Children from 5 to 10 years of age must practise bhastrikā for 1 minute, kapālabhāti 5 times, bāhya prāṇāyāma 3 times, anuloma - viloma for 5 minutes, bhrāmari and udgītha 3 to 5 times and praṇava prāṇāyāma for 1-2 minutes. This will make them strong, intelligent, wise, chaste, energetic, courageous, valiant, proud and industrious. Prāṇāyāma will inculcate self-confidence and self-discipline in children. Prāṇāyāma also increases the concentration of children. It will raise their IQ level and they will have good eyesight and good height. There won't be anger, violence, crime and wantonness in children; they will rather become calm and quiet, sensitive, tolerant, loving, compassionate and affectionate and will love and adore their nation, teachers and parents.

3. Boys/girls from 10 to 18 years of age should do bhastrikā for 2 minutes, kapālabhāti and anuloma–viloma for 10 minites each, bāhya, bhrāmarī and udgītha 5 times each and praṇava prāṇāyāma for 2 to 3 minutes.

4. It a healthy person does kapālabhāti and anuloma-viloma prāṇāyāmas only for 5 minutes each, he can live a life free of diseases and tension. If he does kapālabhāti and anuloma-viloma for 10 minutes each, he can be free of diseases even amidst the enjoyments of life, otherwise indulgence in these enjoyments will cause diseases. If he does kapālabhāti and anuloma-viloma for 15 minutes each he can get rid of common ailments like. B.P., diabetes, asthma, thyroid, joint pains, flatulence, constipation, acidity, etc, and by doing kapālabhāti and anuloma- viloma for 30 minutes each one can even get rid of incurable diseases like cancer.

5. Patients have got a new lease of life by practising prāṇāyāma (for the duration of time shown in the table below) in incurable diseases like cancer, vitiligo/ leucoderma, psoriasis, rheumatic arthritis, etc.

PRĀṆĀYĀMA	APPROXIMATE DURATION	APPROXIMATE NUMBER BY DOING TWICE PER DAY	APPROXIMATE NUMBER PER MONTH	APPROX NUMBER OVER 9 MONTHS
BHASTRIKĀ	10 MTS. TWICE MORN - EVE	240	7200	64800
KAPĀLABHĀTI	30 MINUTES TWICE	3600	108000	972000
BĀHYA	5 MINUTES TWICE	22	660	5940
UJJĀYĪ	5 MINUTES TWICE	22	660	5940
ANULOMA-VILOMA	30 MINUTES TWICE	180	5400	48600
BHRĀMARĪ	5 MINUTES TWICE	22	660	5940
UDGĪTHA	5 MINUTES TWICE	22	660	5940
PRAṆAVA	5 MINUTES TWICE	30	900	8100
GRAND TOTAL				**1117260**

In the table above I have given the quintessence of the experiences of my whole life.

In short, on the basis of my experience so far, I can say that by doing prāṇāyāma in the morning and evening for 1/1/2 hours (i.e. for 3 hours daily) in 9 months the number of all prāṇāyāmas totals to 11 lakh approximately. That means that by doing 11 lakh prāṇāyāmas one gets rid of incurable diseases like cancer, leucoderma, psoriasis, multiple sclerosis, S.L.E. and rheumatic arthritis. The mental and spiritual benefit earned by a seeker (sādhaka) during this period is beyond words. We hear of achieving divine powers (siddhis) by performing 11 lakh japas and yajñas each of gāyatrī and mahāmṛtyuñjaya, etc. , in ancient times. It may be a matter of speculation as to which divine powers are achieved by these performances. But we have got all the proofs of benefits of accomplishments by performing 11 lakh counts of prāṇāyāma.

Mainly kapālabhāti is done approximately 9 lakh times and anuloma-viloma about 51 thousand times under this programme, and by performing these for about 9 months one gets a new lease of life. As a child is born of a mother's womb after 9 months, similarly prāṇa acts as a mother to give you new birth (new lease of life). The seers of Chāndogya Upaniṣad say; **prāṇaḥ pitā prāṇo māta,** i.e., prāṇa is father, prāṇa is mother. As a child is born from father and mother, similarly prāṇas in the form of father and mother give us a new birth. If some hereditary disease or mental disorder has come in our body or mind from the bodies of our parents, yoga dispels that too. We have cured by prāṇāyāma hereditary disease like hypertension, skin disease, asthma and arthritis and the mental flaws and disorders like lust, anger, greed, delusion and egoism.

ABDOMINAL BREATHING – AN UNSCIENTIFIC THEORY

God or Nature has constituted human body in such a way that our windpipe (trachea) is open round the clock. There is a cartilage called epiglottis. When we eat food, it works like a lid to close the trachea when the food is entering inside. Rest of the time it is open. Our tradition prohibits us to talk while eating because the upper end of trachea called larynx helps us in talking and inhaling. Therefore, if we talk while eating, larynx has to work at that time and epiglottis is not able to function as a lid to close the larynx and the food we are eating goes into trachea, which makes us cough. The purpose of this clarification is to make us understand that our oesophagus and trachea are separate tubes. When we eat food it goes straight through the oesophagus (foodpipe) into our stomach, and the breath (prāṇa) goes straight through the trachea (windpipe) into our lungs. And it is an important scientific truth that the organs of our stomach like bowels, liver, intestines, etc., cannot absorb the oxygen. It is only through lungs that blood corpuscles absorb the oxygen and circulate it through the body including the heart. Therefore, 'diaphragmatic deep breathing' or 'thoracic breathing up to diaphragm' is always the best respiratory procedure while doing prāṇāyāma. 'Abdominal breathing' is totally unscientific and useless. The word 'useless' purports to say that if you breathe through abdomen in bhastrikā or anuloma - viloma prāṇāyāmas, you will not be absorbing any oxygen in the abdomen, therefore you will not be able to earn any benefit from prāṇāyāma. One gets the illusion of abdominal breathing because when one takes a deep breath, it always goes into lungs, but with its entry into lungs, the diaphragm, which is exactly between the lungs and stomach, gets bloated, and a layman thinks that the breath is going into abdomen, whereas actually it is quite clear that the breath goes into lungs only. With the bloating of diaphragm one feels that the abdomen is getting bloated. In spite of all these facts if one breathes or makes one breathe through abdomen, his thinking is totally unscientific. Unfortunately, many yoga authorities, due to their incomplete knowledge of physiology, have prescribed deep breathing through abdomen. This runs counter to reason and logic, and is therefore unacceptable.

COMPONENTS OF AIR

The air breathed in by a person is called 'oxygen' and the air breathed out is called 'carbon dioxide.' This is partially true, but the factual position is that the air we breathe in contains a greater part of 'nitrogen', and also the air that we breathe out contains a greater part of nitrogen. However the internal system of our body is such that our blood corpuscles absorb only oxygen from the lungs, and release carbon dioxide. Other components of air like nitrogen and carbon dioxide, etc, are not absorbed by our body. Therefore these components of air like nitrogen, etc. enter our body, but exit back without getting absorbed. The natural respiratory process of plants and trees is quite contrary to that of ours. They breathe in carbon dioxide and breathe out oxygen. Plants grow by absorbing nitrogen through their roots. It is also a divine miracle that one lives on oxygen, while the other lives on carbon dioxide. There is life in both, but the supports of life are different. It is also necessary for equilibrium in nature. Therefore, the constitution of God's biological creation is a great marvel in itself. Therefore, I say it rather light-heartedly that if a man does not return that amount of oxygen by planting trees which he takes for sustaining his life, God makes him a tree in the next birth, and tells him in his birth as a tree to return that amount of oxygen. For the information of readers, we give below the table showing components of air:

COMPONENTS OF AIR

Nitrogen	78.09%
Oxygen	20.95%
Argon	0.93%
Carbon dioxide	0.03%

And minor gases like hydrogen, neon, helium, methane, krypton, etc.

SCIENTIFIC PROOFS OF PRĀṆĀYĀMA

While experimenting with yoga directly or indirectly on millions of people we came across certain results and proofs which are creating a new interest in the field of medicine. In this series of yoga/ experiments/results/proofs, the most scientific and authentic book titled 'Yoga in Synergy with Medical Science' authored by Acharya Balkrishna is a complete scientific proof, which throws light on the scientific clinical reports, comparative studies, pathological reports, right from the clinical control trial to their pre-yoga and post-yoga state, as well as other reports like ECG, PFT, angiography, biopsy, bone mineral density showing the healthy changes occurring on the body after practising yoga vis-a-vis their state of health before practising yoga, in different types of diseases; the book also gives a detailed report on the psychosomatic effect of yoga on millions of patients. Not only this, you will find in the book 'Yoga in Synergy with Medical Science' scientific proofs of almost all the diseases like cancer, AIDS, heart disease, hepatitis, TB, thyroid, leucoderma, psoriasis, rheumatic arthritis, infertility, and MS, etc. having been cured with yoga. I would therefore humbly request my readers that they should read the book 'Yoga in Synergy with Medical Science' at least once and motivate their enlightened friends–doctors, engineers and scientists, here and abroad. This will establish the truth about yoga on global scale, the walls of ignorance, prejudice, selfishness and egoism will collapse, and the world-conquering odyssey of our traditional Vedic science and culture will be completed. May I once again request all my admirers, devotees, worshippers and intelligentsia that they must read 'Yoga in Synergy with Medical Science' and motivate others to read it in order to know the scientific proofs. When all those persons who have a nationalist, spiritualistic, humanitarian and scientific ideology read the book 'Yoga in Synergy with Medical Science', there will surely be a dawn of complete revolution on the medical system of the whole world.

MECHANICAL ANALYSIS OF YOGIC PROCEDURES

The process of respiration goes on at two levels in our body– 1. at the level of blood cells, and 2. at the level of tissue cells. While breathing we perform the respiratory process at both levels. In prāṇāyāma we perform the serial inhalation and exhalation in a balanced manner. Prāṇāyāma improves the circulation of blood in our brain and body, and the functioning of endocrine glands becomes well-regulated, which makes us healthy by destroying the foreign matter in our body and brain. Sprinting and other exercises also give us these benefits because all these activities contribute to the catabolic process in our body and we get health benefits from them due to burning a lot of fat and improvement in blood circulation. But prāṇāyāma not only improves our blood circulation but also regulates the functioning of our endocrine glands. It has been proved that malfunctioning of our endocrine glands is the cause of most diseases like diabetes, thyroid disorders, hypertension, blockage in blood circulation, obesity, brain diseases like depression, illusion, Parkinson's disease, etc. Therefore, we can get rid of all these diseases if the functioning of these glands is well-regulated through prāṇāyāma.

DIFFERENCE BETWEEN ANABOLISM AND CATABOLISM

CATABOLISM	ANABOLISM
• Prevents the excess of protein, fat and carbohydrates. • Provides energy by digesting large accumulations of all of them. • Increases blood sugar, fatty acid. Decreases the immunity factor. • Increases the quantity of liver enzyme and blood cells. • Increases the blood pressure.	• Increases protein, fat and carbohydrates. • Discourages their being digested. Provides immunity by increasing white blood corpuscles. • Increases bone growth. • Increases the functioning of cells, glands and brain. • Decreases the blood pressure and improves the systolic heart rate.

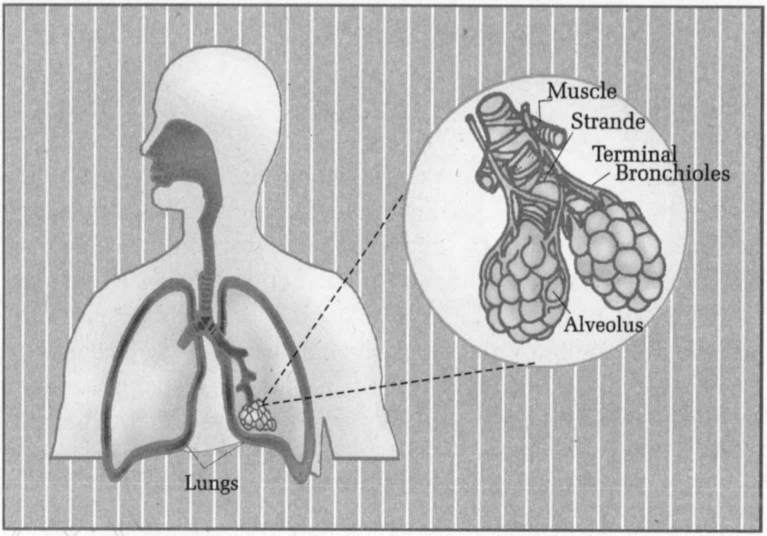

Human lungs and constitution of Alveoli

RESPIRATORY SYSTEM

The main function of respiratory system is to supply oxygen to the cells of body and to expel carbon dioxide, but this fact must not be lost sight of that it is essential that there is a fixed quantity of carbon dioxide in our blood. For the breathing function, the following organs of our body have an important role to play in the respiratory system:

1. Oral cavity
2. Oesophagus
3. Trachea
4. First bronchi
5. Second bronchi
6. Alveoli

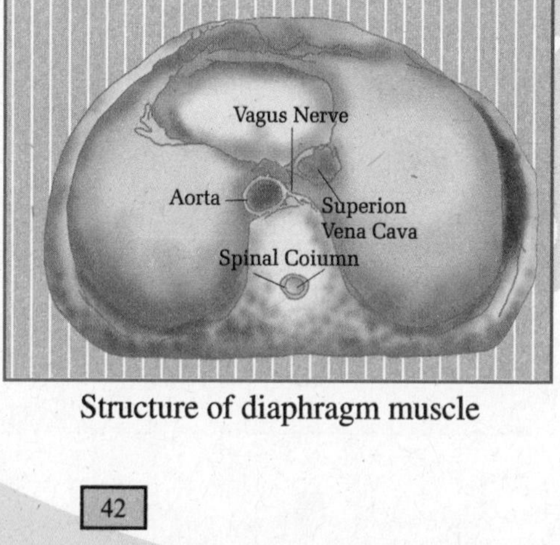

Structure of diaphragm muscle

Alveoli is the tiniest unit of the respiratory system where O and CO_2 are entering and exiting. There are approximately 300 million alveoli in one lung. Their surface area comes to 75-100 sq. metres. Oxygen (O) enters the blood stream through alveoli and CO_2 travels from the blood stream into alveoli.

Between inhaling and exhaling, ribs and sternum swell up and the diaphragm subsides, which expands the width of chest and the pressure in lungs is reduced and oxygen enters into lungs. The principal unit of the respiratory system is the diaphragm. This muscle joins together the peritoneal cavity , pleural cavity and spinal cord. The yogic procedures propagated by Swamiji cause contraction and expansion of diaphragm. In prāṇāyāma we are instructed to breathe slowly and deeply, by which the diaphragm moves down and prāṇa (air) has maximum circulation.

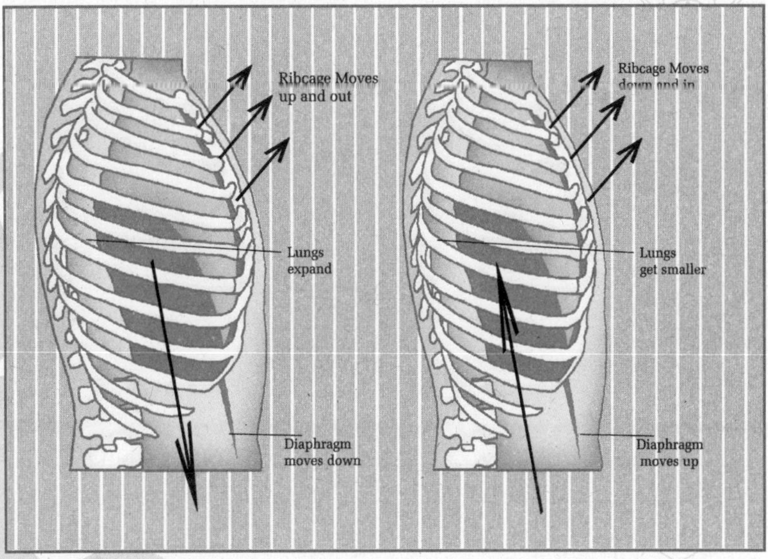

The movement in chest cavity during the process of respiration

Oxygen is the most essential element to activate the cells of body. The procedure which increases the quantity of oxygen in lungs and increases the expulsion of carbon dioxide from lungs is called prāṇāyāma. By prāṇāyāma, along with the abundant increase in the level of oxygen in blood, the level of carbon dioxide also goes up. Here it is very necessary to know as to how oxygen impacts the cells functionally.

FUNCTIONAL EFFECTS OF PRĀṆĀYĀMA

The following functional effects can be seen in the body by doing prāṇāyāma:

1. Availability of more oxygen for combustion purpose
2. Benefits associated with lymphatic system
3. Benefits to the brain and nervous system

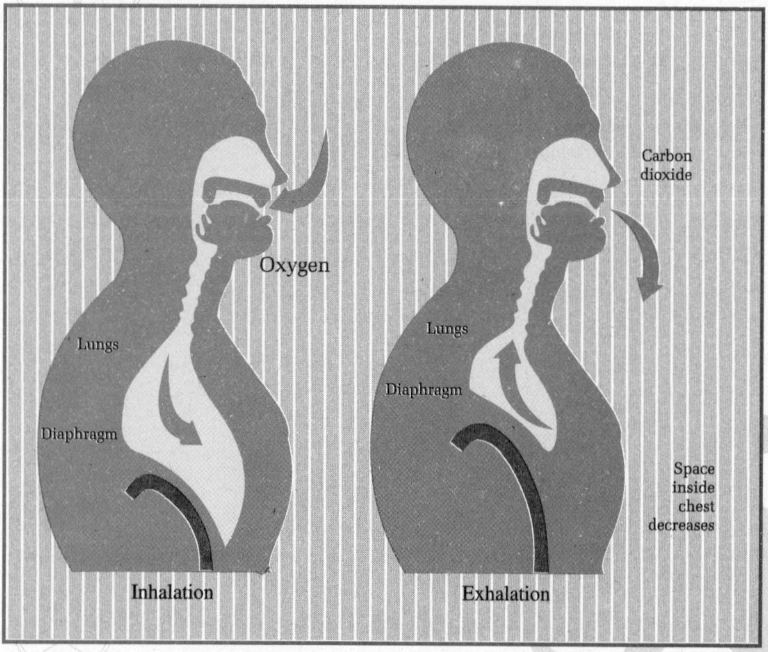

The Mechanism of breathing

PROPER COMBUSTION OF OXYGEN

Without oxygen, all the systems in human body can disintegrate in a short while and die. Therefore it is generally a significant matter for all the systems that if the body can get more oxygen anyhow, it will work as a medicine on all the diseases of organs of the body, and even those diseases and disorders can be cured by adequate supply of oxygen which are caused due to inadequate supply to the cells. When a person performs any physical activity, the body needs more oxygen. Modern research has proved it that with the increase in demand of oxygen in the blood during the course of any physical activity, there is regulated metabolism of oxygen. Modern research and medical tests have also confirmed this fact that the cause of various diseases in the body is the lack of proper combustion of oxygen. Although research over the past few years has also proved that the main cause behind highly consumptive diseases and other disorders of this type is the poor supply of oxygen.

With the regular practice of prāṇāyāma oxygen is supplied which

(a) generates energy

(b) along with the generation of energy, water is generated in the cells which helps regulate the flow of lymphs.

(a) GENERATION OF ENERGY

For all functions of all the cells of our body and for regulating the body temperature, all the energy is generated by the chemical reaction of oxygen and sugar. Whenever the normal metabolism rate of the body increases, the body requires more oxygen; and to meet this increased demand of oxygen, our inhalation-exhalation speed also increases. This can be understood by the following process:

$$\text{fuel, i.e., glucose+oxygen} = \text{energy+}CO_2\text{+water}$$

(b) GENERATION OF WATER

Another significant benefit obtained through the combustion of oxygen metabolism by virtue of the practice of prāṇāyāma is related to lymphatic system. Depending on the utilisation of more and more oxygen by the cells, the quantity of water in the body increases which proves to be very useful in the internal cleansing of our body.

(c) IMMUNITY

In the process of inhalation during bhastrikā prāṇāyāma the blood pressure increases, and with the process of exhalation there is reduction in blood pressure. If the practice of this prāṇāyāma goes on regularly for 5 minutes, all the organs in our abdomen, including the endocrine glands, feel the vibration. The process of this vibration can be understood through the following diagrams:

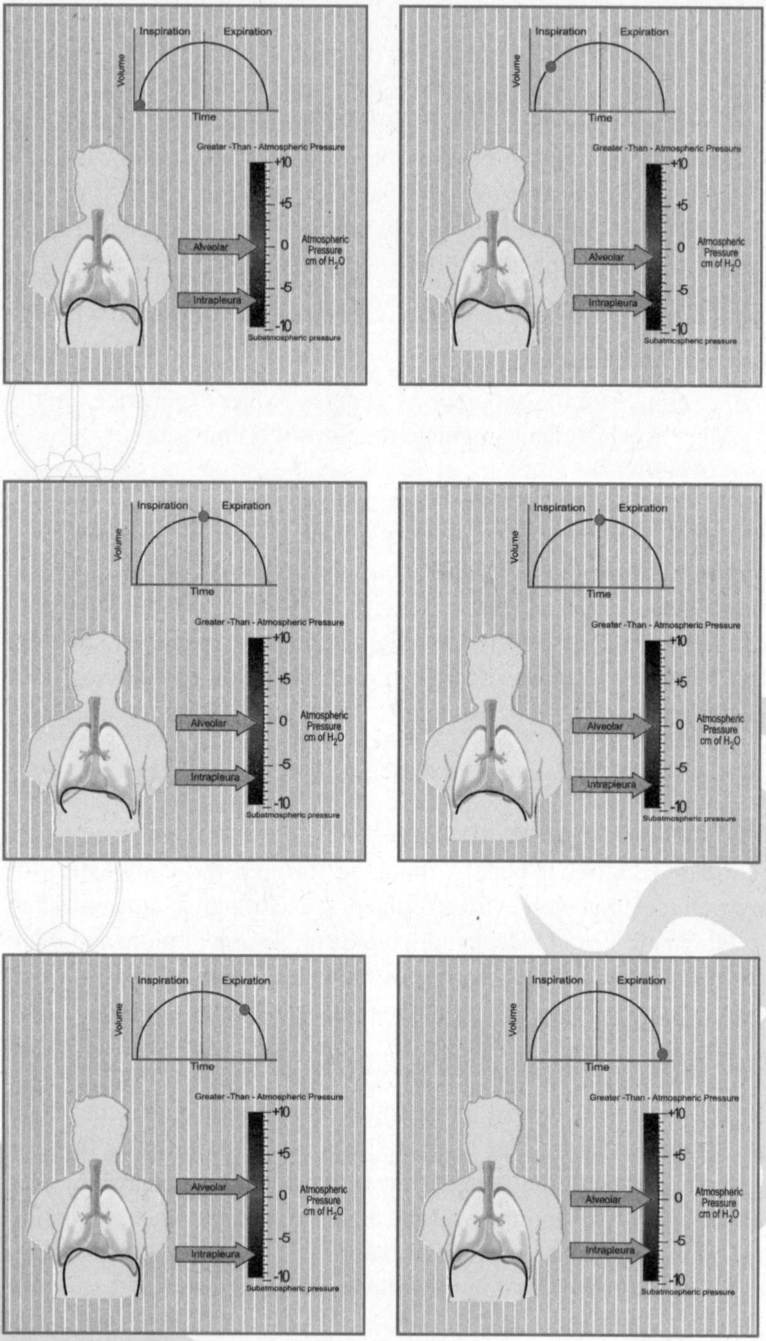
Inspiration
Expiration
Volume
Time
Greater -Than - Atmospheric Pressure
+10
+5
0
-5
-10
Alveolar
Intrapleura
Atmospheric Pressure cm of H_2O
Subatmospheric pressure

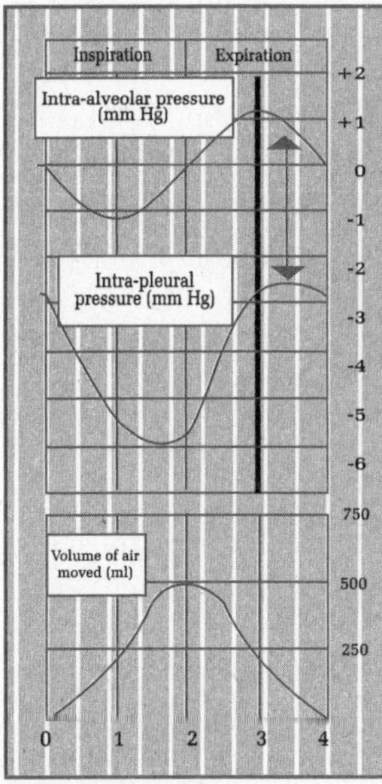

Pressure air 15 rounds of Breathing per minute

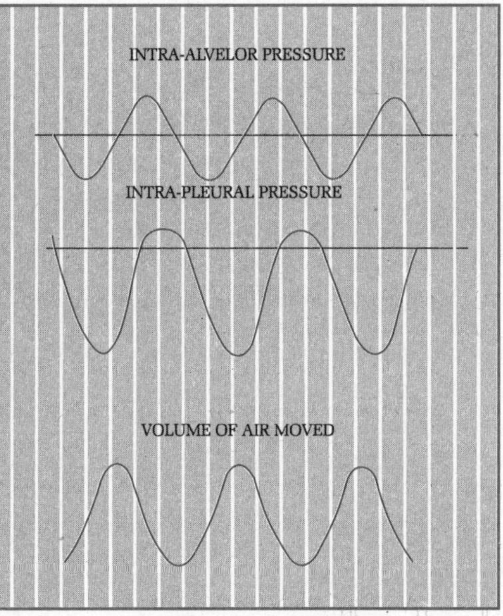

Position of pressure volume vibration during bhastrikā prāṇāyāma at fast speed

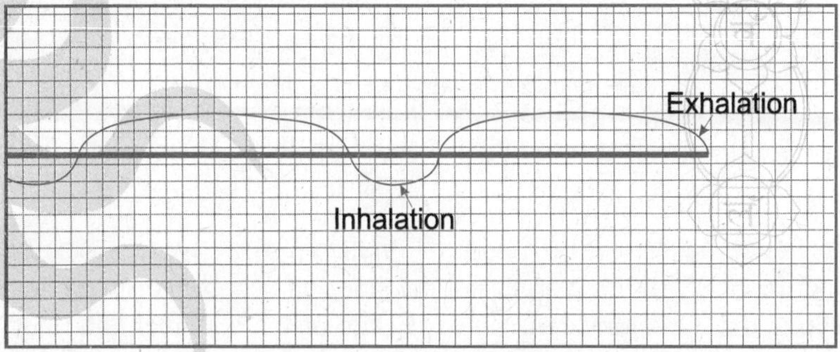

POSITION OF PRESSURE VOLUME VIBRATION DURING NORMAL BREATHING

In this position, if the inhalation is for 1 second and the exhalation takes 3 seconds, no vibrations are produced in the organs and glands in the body.

Normally in one round of breathing (i.e., one inhalation–exhalation) we use 500 ml (Tidal Volume) air. Studies prove that if we take a deep breath, the quantity of the breathed air can go up to 4500 ml and if one's lungs have adequate vital capacity, it can go up to 8000 ml (8 litres). By this deep inhaling and vigorous exhaling the level of oxygen in blood increases, which supplies adequate prāṇa-vāyu to the tissues in cells.

KAPĀLABHĀTI PRĀṆĀYĀMA

In kapālabhāti prāṇāyāma there is normal inhalation and forced exhalation. In the process of forced exhalation there is a contraction and relaxation activity in the diaphragm and abdominal muscles, which has a beneficial effect on various organs of the stomach (large

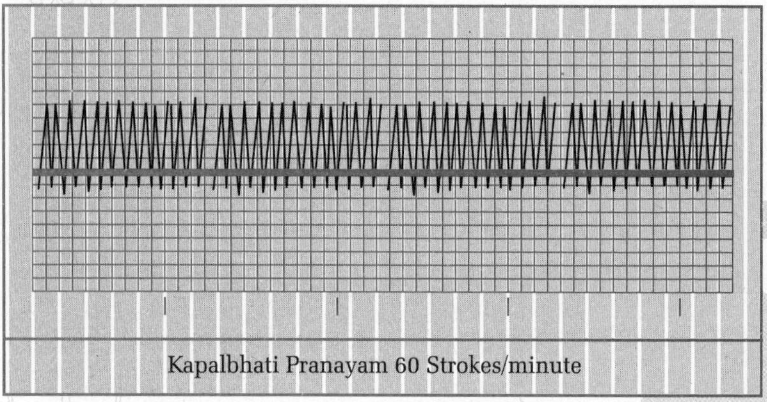

The speed of respiration during Kapalbhati Pranayam

intestine, pancreas, liver, spleen, small intestine, colon, kidneys, uterus, etc.). All these organs of the stomach become so strong and active due to contraction and expansion of the abdomen that they start supplying all sorts of vital juices required by the body. The secretion from endocrine glands is then neither too high nor too low. Thus by exerting repeated pressure on the diaphragam through kapālabhāti prāṇāyāma, one can succeed in the great endeavour of keeping the body-machine fit as a fiddle.

This procedure increases the intravenous blood pressure and the blood comes back to the heart forcefully, resulting in an unprecedented beneficial effect on the heart. The speed and pulsation achieved by us through prāṇāyāma is achieved in modern medicine by EECP[1] procedure. In the EECP procedure the lower part of the leg (calves) and pelvic region are tied with cuffs and about 60 external strokes are given per minute. Modern medicine regards this procedure as an alternative of coronary angioplasty and bye-pass surgery. The rate of EECP is regulated according to the heart pulsation rate, which creates vibration in the arteries, which removes any blockages in the arteries. We can accomplish this procedure by prāṇāyāma as well, because we create vibration/pulsations by prāṇāyāma too, which help remove the blockages in blood vessels, and by doing prāṇāyāma regularly such blockages will not build up again.

We may elucidate the aforesaid procedure by one more example. When the battalion of an army marches past over a bridge, it is ordered to 'mark time', with a view to testing whether the resonance generated by the combination of the natural frequency of that bridge and the forced frequency of the battalion 'marking time' is strong enough to make the bridge crumble. The benefit of this principle of resonance comes to us through the resonance generated by the union of the forced frequency of prāṇāyāma and the natural frequency of heart and arteries, as a result of which the blood clots in the arteries dissolve and flow into the blood stream. Consequently, this removes the blockage of arteries.

Let us take one more example. When the bus does not move, i.e., when it is standing, but its engine is revved up, then, at times, a resonance develops between the natural frequency of the bus and the forced frequency of the engine which creates a sort of tremor in the whole bus, which is even felt by the passengers sitting in the bus. Like those passengers sitting in the bus, clots of blood settle in our arteries here and there, which are forced to flow into the blood stream on getting dissolved by the resonance generated by prāṇāyāma. Consequently, the blockage of arteries is removed and bye-pass surgery, etc., is dispensed with.

1. Enhanced External Counter Pulsation

PRĀṆA (VITAL ENERGY)

As there are many areas of energy and force in the Universe, similarly there is prāṇa-śakti (life-force) in our body, which is linked with our inhaling-exhaling process through an outer field. If there is any imbalance or leakage of this prāṇa-śakti, we develop diseases. Therefore, we can keep this prāṇa-śakti balanced by the co-ordination of prāṇa and udāna. Hence, consciousness (caitanya) is attained by us through this process of inhaling and exhaling.

RESPIRATION AND CEREBRUM

For the process of respiration nostrils are most indispensable. It is by these nostrils that the inhaled prāṇa-vāyu (life air) is purified and the temperature is controlled. Nostrils which are a part of our skull give such a structure to the cerebrum that there is not the least possibility of any organ of the cerebrum leaking through. It is the cerebrum which sends signals for respiratory process and controls it, but very few people know that the cerebrum also has a respiratory function which keeps it active, and it is only through the respiratory function performed by the cerebrum that the circulation of energy received from solar rays and prāṇa-vāyu is possible in the human body. Oriental philosophers and Ayurveda experts believe that the cerebrum also performs functions like respiration, pulsation, etc.

CEREBROSPINAL FLUID

The cerebrospinal fluid present in the cerebrum regulates the messenger neuropeptides at the level of cells, which play a very important role in harmonising various functions of the body. The cerebrospinal fluid circulates at the junction of cerebrum and spinal cord (suṣumṇā kāṇḍa) The two pumps fixed in the mechanism used in its circulation work in the spinal cord. The cranium pump is fixed at the surface and the sacrum pump is fixed at the bottom. In the process of prāṇāyāma when one breathes in and breathes out, there is contraction and expansion of diaphragm by which both the pumps regulating the cerebrospinal fluid get activated, and this contraction helps the sacral pump circulate the cerebrospinal fluid in the cerebrum, and while exhaling the cerebrospinal fluid is circulated in the spinal cord.

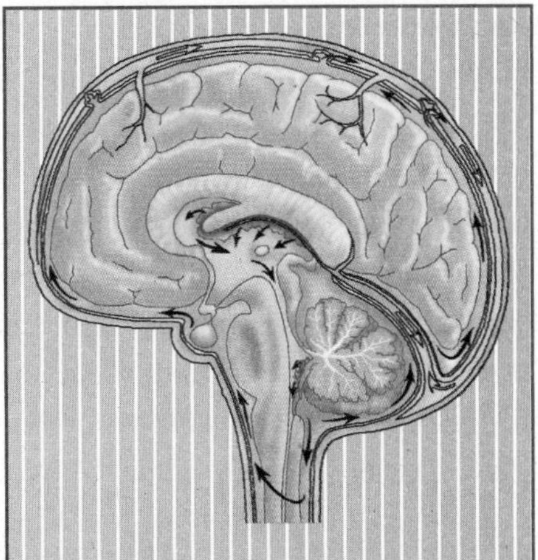

REGULATING AIR RACE OF OFREBRO SPINAL FLUID IN CERRBRUM AND SUṢMNĀ KĀṆḌA DURING PRĀṆĀYĀMA

NEUROPCPTIDES

The molecules working as messengers in the cerebrospinal fluid are called 'neuropeptides' They exchange the signals regulating all the physical activities in the nervous system, and perform the function of maintaining harmony between the cerebrum and other organs, at the level of cells. Through various researches, more than 100 neuropcptides have been identified so far. Neuropeptides not only perform the physical activities of the body, but also control the emotional activities going on in human cerebrum. They perform a very important function of transmitting to the cerebrum signals of pain being felt in the body. The pain-relieving medicines being prescribed at present connect with the receptors located on these neuropeptides, which relieves the pain. Among the pain-relieving medicines prescribed so far, the molecules of morphin are most

BRAIN HEMISPHERES

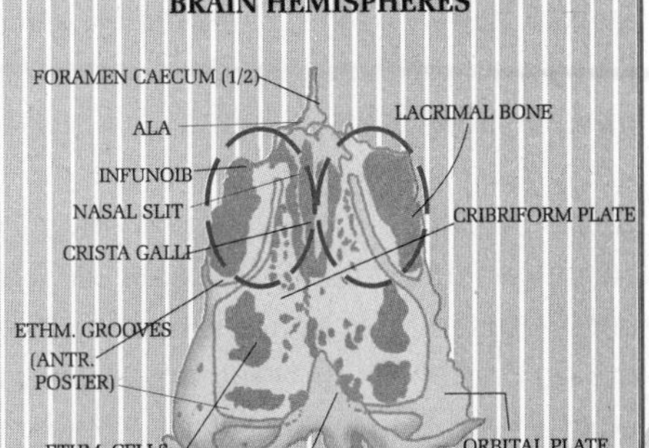

BRAIN HEMISPHERE INSIDE THE CEREBRUM

capable of connecting with the receptors of these neuropcptides, which makes it the most widely used pain reliever, but all that is temporary. This action in prāṇāyāma occurs due to pulsations in the hermetic cavity as a result of developing of intracranial pressure between the cerebrum and spinal cord by the circulation of cerebrospinal fluid. When the circulation of cerebrospinal fluid is at its climax, our cerebrum is in its extremely active and conscious state. In modern research, efforts are being made to identify the sound produced in this procedure as well as the waves created in cerebrospinal fluid. This state is also achieved by anuloma-viloma and bhrāmarī prāṇāyāma in which both left and right parts of the cerebrum are activated equally. The mechanics of the state of anuloma-viloma prāṇāyāma can be understood in the following manner.

The Third Eye

In modern medicine great significance is being attached to the principle "use of both brain hemispheres by nāḍīs", propounded by yoga in early times. In yoga, the nāḍī has been stated to be the medium of physical, mental and spiritual energy flowing in human body. There are more than 72000 nāḍīs in the body but of all these nāḍīs iḍā (parasympathetic), piṅgalā (sympathetic) and suṣumṇā (central) are most important. Normally either iḍā or piñgalā remains active; the suṣumṇā is normally inactive. During respiration, the prāṇa-vāyu entering the body either travels through iḍā or through piṅgalā. Iḍā (candra-svara) nāḍī starts from the left nostril which joins the right nostril. Thus the prāṇa-vāyu flowing inside first enters cerebellum and medulla oblongata, then travels to the left of suṣumṇā kāṇḍa (central spinal cord), and finishes its journey at the end of suṣumṇā kāṇḍa. Similarly , in the exactly opposite direction the function of circulating prāṇa vāyu is performed by piṅgalā nāḍī (sūrya-svara). In each nostril located on the internal cells of the nose there are passages made of tissues called cartilages which are fully controlled by ājñā- cakra (mental centre). During respiration, when one nostril opens, at that time the entry of breath through the other nostril is completely suspended. On the ceiling of the nose where both the nostrils join each other and wherefrom iḍā and piṅgalā nāḍīs originate, there lies the main vital spot of the body. It is here that iḍā (parasympathetic nerve) and piṅgalā (sympathetic nerve) join to make a plexus, called ājñā- cakra.

In our life-discipline scriptures this has been called 'the third eye'. The seeker who is able to activate this spot attains unique power.

Effect of anuloma-viloma prāṇāyāma (Alternate Nostril Breathing)

We find that the alternation of cerebral dominance depends also on the breathing round of each nostril. According to modern science this atternation is regulated by the action of sympathetic and parasympathetic nervous system. (To understand the meaning of these words, see the diagram.)

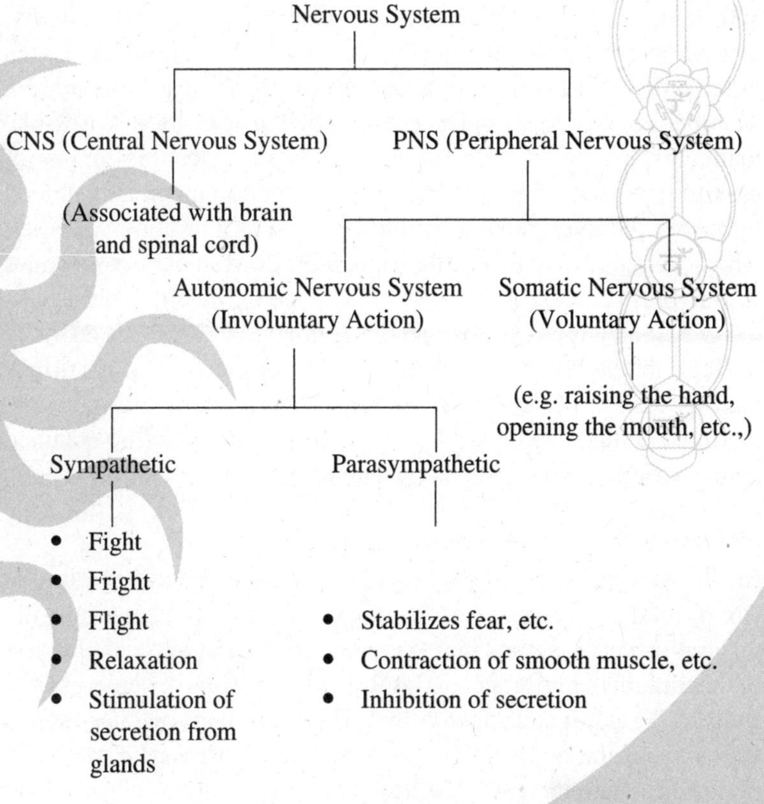

On the basis of the principle of yogic science "use of both brain hemispheres by nādīs", this alternation is regulated by iḍā and piṅgalā nādīs. Complete harmony is established between the functions of both brain hemispheres through anuloma-viloma prāṇāyāma. In this state balance is achieved due to the prāṇa-vāyu entering through both nostrils. We find that during inhalation the circulation of cerebrospinal fluid is from the spine toward the brain, while during exhalation it is from the brain toward the spine.

With the harmony in the flow of prāṇā-vāyu the position of the circulation of cerebrospinal fluid is also harmonised. With this harmony there is proper distribution of vital energy to all the cells, tissues and organs of the body, and their functioning gets stream-lined.

Anuloma-viloma prāṇāyāma, a natural and spontaneous procedure, also regulates the concentration of oxygen and carbon dioxide in the blood. As the high concentration of CO_2 in the blood makes it acidic and de-oxygenated and causes a host of fatal diseases, similarly, instead of taking resort to prāṇāyāma, if the concentration of oxygen in the blood is raised to a high level by artificial means like oxygen chamber or oxygen cylinder, etc., it can cause many diseases like lenticular opacity (the hardening of eye lenses leading to loss of eyesight), whereas the right amount of oxygen supplied to the blood improves the eyesight, the whole body starts pulsating with life, which we see everyday. For the regular production of neuropeptides in our brain the right quantity of CO_2 is as much necessary as oxygen. If a high level of oxygen is supplied to the body by artificial devices, the desirable ratio of O and CO_2 for our body is disturbed. On this basis we can say that anuloma-viloma prāṇāyāma can cure the most complicated diseases. All this benefit cannot be obtained from artificial devices like oxygen chamber, etc.,

Stressed state

In the state of stress the sympathetic system of the autonomic (involuntary) nervous system is extremely active, making the respiration very fast with the excessive use of chest muscles. The use of diaphragm in this process is almost 'nil'. The flow of cerebrospinal fluid (CSF) is fast and uncontrolled. Therefore, an incessant stressed state attacks the body and mind with various diseases. The climax of stressed state increases the heart rate, respiration rate and blood pressure. It is this state which we call 'stressed state'. The only way to get rid of this malady is slow, deep and alternate breathing which can be achieved through prāṇāyāma. Parasympathetic activation and tissue regeneration can be achieved through prāṇāyāma. This is the contraction stage of metabolism which is known as 'anabolism'. The climax of this stage is Reduction Response (RR) in which there is a reduction in heart rate, respiration rate and blood pressure. This is the basic rest-activity alternation.

There are two frequencies in the brain–alpha and beta. During prāṇāyāma the frequency of brain is within the limit of 'alpha' frequency. The constant practice of prāṇāyāma makes other harmful waves ineffective.

The 'alpha' level cerebral function is the result of relaxation which promotes health.

Heart Rate Variability (HRV) and Respiration Frequency

The heart is called healthy in proportion to the smoothness of heart Rate Variability (HRV). A low HRV is indicative of heart disease. In a healthy person there is fast increase in heart rate due to excessive exercise like Tread Mill Walk, etc. The heart rate accelerates with the activity of sympathetic and parasympathetic system of autonomic nervous system, whereas the HRV remains controlled during prāṇāyāma procedure, as shown in the diagram below:

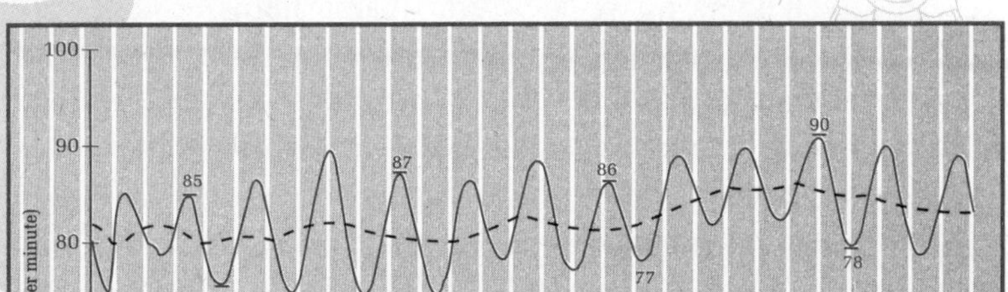

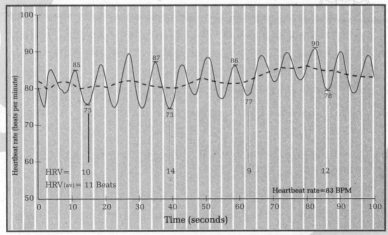

CONTROLLED HRV FREQUENCIES DURING PRĀṆĀYĀMA

A survey shows that in normal conditions the breathing rhythm of an adult during rest/ light work/ heavy work will be as shown in the diagram below:

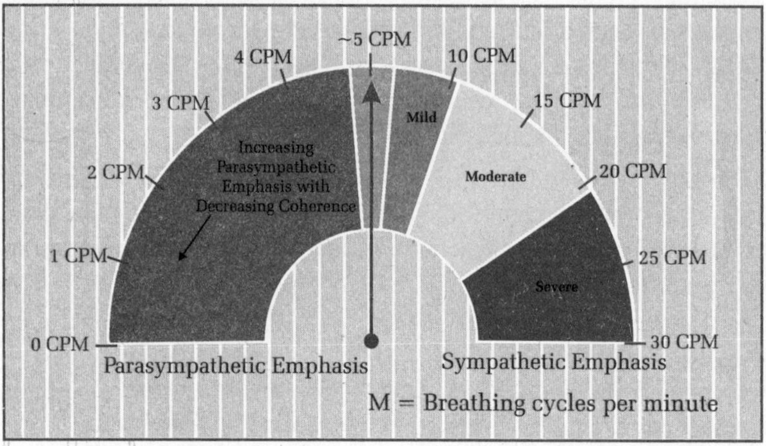

1. As shown in the diagram, in frequency 'A'there will be one round in 12 seconds and 5 rounds per minute.
2. In this position the cardiopulmonary efficiency and dominance will be in the maximum position.

Conclusion

The given facts prove how prāṇāyāma helps cure all the diseases. In the present- day scenario there is a lot of hype about prāṇāyāma, but its full benefit can be achieved when it is done according to correct rules and methods. For this purpose it is essential to know as to what functional changes are caused by prāṇāyāma in our body.

- Prāṇāyāma is a special type of procedure done in a methodical way.
- Prāṇāyāma is an anabolistic procedure which balances and streamlines our blood circulation.
- It is essential for the diaphragm to be involved in the breathing process in prāṇāyāma. This produces vibrations in the abdominal organs and essential blood vessels.

- Kapālabhāti and bhastrikā not only remove blockages in arteries but, if done regularly, even the possibility of their rebuilding up is eliminated. Even the emotional system benefits from the diaphragmatic contraction and expansion.
- The functioning of endocrine glands is balanced and streamlined by prāṇāyāma.
- Through Nāḍī Vijñāna we come to know about the benefits from maintaining the balance in cerebrum through the process of breathing with alternate nostrils in anuloma- viloma
- There is a strong nexus among the respiratory rate, heart rate and cerebral nervous system. With the slowing of respiratory rate this nexus is strengthened all the more and there is a feeling of spiritual serenity, the high blood pressure gets normal, the blood sugar gets to the desirable range and the heart rate becomes normal.
- Therefore, prāṇāyāma is the easiest and cheapest way to spiritual elevation and physical healthiness.

Prāṇa as the Nanotechnology of Medical Science

Nanotechnology is a technical term for those things and instruments which operate at 'nano' scale. From the point of view of metric system, 'nano' means the one billionth (10^{-9}) part of a metre. Seen in the context of 'nano', we have nano materials, nano electronics, nano instruments and nano powders. Mainly it means the activity of material which can be measured in nanometres.

In terms of size, we can think of the red blood corpuscles in human body which are 2000 nanometres long and are outside the nanometre scale. Similarly, there is oxygen which is a part of human body and has active participation in all the chemical activities and metabolism process of the body. For an exercise like prāṇāyāma we made use of oxygen at 'nano' level for all the processes in the body. Nanotechnology is extremely effective and is made use of in the manufacture of artificial (prosthetic) bones which are strong like steel but lighter than natural bones. Similarly, if the intake and release of oxygen is done in special way through various prāṇāyāmas and exercises, it has proved beneficial in several serious ailments like heart disease, angina, rheumatic diseases, etc. At the same time, it has a very beneficial effect on the health as a whole.

The whole universe is created with the union of earth, fire, air, water and ether, and there is an element, viz. prāṇa, which lies at the root of all these five elements.

By the induction of nitrogen into the inanimate world the scientists have given birth to 'green revolution'. Many inventions, like bombs, are afoot with hydrogen, carbon, etc. in the field of science. The medical science has so far made use of oxygen for emergency medicine, and it seems the day is not far when prāṇa-tatva will be used for the treatment of all diseases. Oxygen is the main element in semen and ovum, the basic seeds of the birth of our body; it sustains motility in the sperm and nourishes the ovum. The Upaniṣads call the body 'annamaya'. Anna means food which contains oxygen as its main constituent. The various nutrients of our body taken by us in the form of pulses, grains, vegetables, milk, fruit, etc. contain oxygen as their main constituent, carbohydrates, proteins, fat, minerals, vitamins, etc. are the main constituents of the food giving nourishment to our body, though there are other elements too besides oxygen in our body and universe. In our body structure also there are other elements like carbon, nitrogen, hydrogen, etc. besides oxygen, but it is only oxygen that infuses our body, constituted with five elements and seven types of tissues (dhātus), with vitality, vigour and sentience. The smallest unit of the body is a cell and its nucleus is its brain, and it is mitochondria where energy is generated. It is the oxygen which gives movement and force both to nucleus and mitochondria. The yajña of our life, which is called matabolism in science, is being conducted with oxygen. Oxygen and glucose have main role to play in the generation of energy in each cell of the body. The internal and external functions of the body are performed properly with the proper generation of energy in the mitochondria inside the cell. It is mainly the oxygen which causes the generation of new cells, their decay and the storing of energy.

Oxygen is mainly responsible for preventing the destructive process in the body and for strengthening the constructive and regulatory forces. These days a person is ravaged by a formidable war inside due to lack of physical exertion, stress, unfavourable diet, irregular routine and unrestrained life. This results in the imbalance of doṣas–vāta, pitta and kapha. Put in the jargon of modern medical science, due to poor 'anabolism-catabolism' 'homeostasis' is not being achieved. The imbalance of these doṣas causes depression which in turn causes hypertension, diabetes, obesity, heart disease, dyspepsia, insomnia and even incurable diseases like cancer.

This imbalance of doṣas, disorder of digestion fire, imbalance of tissues in our body, deposit of waste products, unhappiness of our mind and psyche have contributed to our bad health. It has upset the balance of internal secretion of hormones and chemicals. We have to take resort to various medicines as a corrective measure.

On the basis of our prāṇāyāma experiments conducted on millions of people so far, we have come to the conclusion that each cell of our body is endowed with the potential of cloning us, replicating us. We can achieve complete health by giving exercise to our internal organs and by positive thinking, through a full dose of oxygen to the tiniest unit of this body as well as to its every organ and to the functions performed by those organs of our body. Oxygenated blood, internal micro exercise and positive lifestyle–this is what prāṇāyāma tantamounts to. Through bhastrikā, anuloma- viloma, etc. we supply full oxygen to the blood corpuscles of our body, and through kapālabhāti, etc. we circulate energy in our internal organs by speeding them up in a scientific manner, and by awakening faith, dedication, sincerity and belief at mental plane through bhrāmarī, udgītha, etc. we start living a healthy and care-free life.

In this project as a whole oxygen forms the basis of our entire process. As we saw the light of day, the moment we were born we indeliberately took a long breath by way of crying. That was the beginning of the internal functions of our whole body with the awakening of our cerebral energy; our parents made us do prāṇāyāma by making us cry. The oxygen inhaled through prāṇāyāma and the scientifically complete internal exercise and relaxation provided by prāṇāyāma administer self-healing to our body. Prāṇāyāma is self-medicine and self-treatment. It gives us relief from most of the nodules and, to some extent, from spinal surgery, as well as from heart surgery. Then we feel that prāṇāyāma is an amazing technique of 'self operation'. When the anabolism level of the body gets constantly upgraded and the catabolism level gets downgraded through prāṇāyāma, the aging process also slows down, i.e., by dodging past untimely old age we live longer. On the basis of evidence of scientific results of the experiments of prāṇāyāma we can say that when praṇa (i.e. oxygen) is infused into our body by certain well-defined procedures, in a certain fixed quantity in a certain fixed duration of time with an attitude of right thinking, positive changes start occurring automatically in the body and prāṇa starts working as a complete medicine. This is the basic tenet of Yoga Science. This is the basic tenet of health, and this is the basis of building up a nation of healthy, prosperous and perceptive individuals. The manifestation of Prāṇa Vidyā emanates from Vedas is this way:

ā vāta vāhi bheṣajaṁ vi vāta vāhi yadrapaḥ /
tvaṁ hi viśvabheṣajo devānāṁ dūta īyase //(Ṛgveda 10.137.3)

"Prāṇa (i.e. oxygen) is a medicine. It flows inside our body in various forms, and it is not merely a medicine, it is viśvabheṣaja (a panacea), a complete medicine. It is the carrier of whatever is celestial in Nature." Prāṇa is a 'holistic treatment'; the basis of prāṇa is 'complete health'. We have a very authentic and scientific

evidence in our scriptures of the emotional changes in our body that are infused by prāṇa, along with physical or bodily changes.
The seer of Chāndogya Upaniṣad says:-

> **prāṇo ha pitā prāṇo mātā prāṇo bhrātā /**
> **prāṇaḥ svasā prāṇa āeāryaḥ prāṇo brāhmaṇaḥ //**

(ÇHANDOGYA 7.15.1)

The emotional changes occurring in the mind of an individual along with bodily changes, through various procedures of yoga or prāṇa, are authentic and scientific to the same extent as the physical changes. To the individuals gripped by deadly mental disorders like depression and schizophrenia along with physicial diseases, the advice of seers in the yoga tradition is : "O man! Don't get perplexed, discouraged or unsteady. Don't live with a feeling of loneliness or insecurity. You need not be despondent or desperate. Seek the refuge of prāṇa, and practise prāṇāyāma. This prāṇa is your father, mother, brother and sister. Prāṇa is your preceptor and seeker of brahman." Here prāṇas have been described metaphorically, i.e., by depicting prāṇas as father, etc., the seers of Upaniṣads hint at their emotional impact. Pitā (father) means 'pāti rakṣati iti pitā; mānyaṁ hitaṁ karoti iti mātā, i.e., one who protects is father, and one who does good to you with love, affection, sincerity, sacrifice, patience, perseverance, compassion and bravery is mother; brother is one who supports you and brings you up; preceptor is one who purifies our conduct, speech, behaviour, temperament and thinking; and brāhmaṇa is one who helps you in knowing or revealing brahman. Prāṇa as a mother penetrates to our innermost heart which makes the heart in our body healthy. We have confirmed all this with scientific evidence; but more than that, prāṇāyāma infuses our heart with the love, affection, compassion and sensitivity of a mother. With the practice of prāṇāyāma we start getting more affectionate. A feeling of patience, energy, courage, valour, austerity, sacrifice and dedication starts awakening in us. A despondent, desperate person afflicted by miseries of the world finds himself free of all depressing feelings, and sways enraptured under the blessings of prāṇa. Prāṇa as a brother gives bodily and emotional support. As a preceptor it purifies our conduct, our life. Prāṇa exerts a direct influence on our thinking. When the thoughts get purified through prāṇāyāma, the food and conduct of a person get purified. Therefore, one who practises prāṇāyāma marches forward on the path of restraint and good conduct abstaining himself from violence, crime, theft, dishonesty, misconduct, profligacy, etc. He becomes a sensitive man of character. This is what is needed most in modern times. Prāṇāyāma is the only solution to growing disbelief, violence, crime, corruption, dishonesty, sexuality and vice, and prāṇa, through the purification of our life, leads us to the most sacred brahman. It makes us experience the Absolute Truth, the Absolute Bliss. Prāṇāyāma helps us attain samādhi, putting an end to all our afflictions and bestowing upon us attainment of self-manifestation, self-enlightenment, self-knowledge, self-realization, liberated existence, non-attachment and steady intellect.

prāṇasyedaṁ vasé sarvaṁ yat tridive pratiṣṭhitam /
māteva putrān rakṣasva śrīśca prajñāṁ ca vidhehi na iti //
(PRAŚNOPANIṢAD 2.13)

"All the three spheres of this universe are under the control of prāṇa. O Prāṇa, Lord of the universe! Protect us children as a mother. Give us prosperity and intellect. "The corner-stone of material development and spiritual elevation is the prāṇāyāma-oriented lifestyle. The twenty-first century is the century of union of science and spiritualism, and the basic tenet of this century is prāṇāyāma. Our scriptures speak volumes of the pranic energy:

prāṇā vāva vasavaḥ / (CHĀ. UP. 3.16.1)
prāṇā vāva rudrāḥ / (CHĀ. UP. 3.16.3)
prāṇā vāva ādityāḥ / (CHĀ. UP. 3.16.5)

" Prāṇas are Vasus, i.e., the base for settling life (ete hīdaṁ sarvaṁ vāsayanti), prāṇas are Rudras to destroy the diseases (ete hīdaṁ sarvaṁ rodayanti), and prāṇas are Ādityas to save the life from snapping or prāṇas embrace all (ete hīdaṁ sarvamādadate).

In this book we have also presented the evidence of scientific documentation of emotional effects of prāṇāyāma. On the basis of the traditional Vedic lore of prāṇāyāma as well as on the basis of scientific research and investigations on the experiments of prāṇāyāma in the light of Vedic lore, we can now say that in the modern age when the scientific world is heading for nanotechnology in every field, what else can be the nanotechnology of medical science except 'prāṇa'?

IMPORTANCE AND BENEFITS OF PRĀṆĀYĀMA

The control (āyāma) of prāṇa (breath) is prāṇāyāma. All the actions of our body are directly or indirectly connected with prāṇa. The unbreakable link of life and death with each individual all the time coincides with prāṇa only. In Sanskrit, the word 'jīvana' is derived from vjiva (prāṇa dhāraṇe), and the word 'mṛtyu' is derived from vmṛṅ (prāṇatyāge). Our Vedas, scriptures and Upaniṣads sing the eternal glory of prāṇa to no end. Atharvaveda says: **prāṇāpānau mṛtyormā pāta svāhā.** 'May both prāṇa and apāṇa protect me from death.' Here is what Manu says about prāṇāyāma:

dahyante dhmāyamānānāṁ dhātūnāṁ hi yathā malāḥ /
tathendriyāṇāṁ dahyante doṣāḥ prāṇasya nigrahāt //

(MANU : 6.71)

"As the dross matter, impurities of metals like gold, etc. are destroyed when they are heated in fire, similarly flaws of senses and mind are also dispelled by prāṇāyāma." Haṭhayogapradīpikā says:

prāṇāyāmaireva sarve praśuṣyanti malā iti /
ācāryāṇāntu keṣāñcidanyat karma na sammatam //

(HA. PRA : 2.38)

There is no activity more noteworthy than pranayama for the removal of obstructions to waste expulsion. By doing the various pranayamas, all the dross matter of the body, mind & senses dries up.

āsanena rujaṁ hanti prāṇāyāmena pātakam /
vikāraṁ mānasaṁ yogī pratyāhāreṇa muñcati //

(YOGACŪḌĀMAṆYUPANIṢAD 109)

A yogi dispels rajoguṇa (flippancy) by āsana, pāpa (sins) by prāṇāyāma and mental disorders by pratyāhāra (withdrawal).

cale vāte calaṁ cittaṁ niścale niścalaṁ bhavet.

(HA. PRA.: 2.2)

There is an intimate relation between prāṇa and mind. With the stabilization of prāṇa, the mind concentrates automatically.

Yogadarśana also says : **tataḥ kṣīyate prakaśāvaraṇaṁ; dhāraṇāsu ca yogyatā manasaḥ.** **(YOGADARŚANA 2.52,53)**

By practising prāṇāyāma, the screen of darkness of evil, ignorance and misery covering the mind decays. In the purged and purified mind, dhāraṇā (concentration) takes place automatically, and with the help of concentration one moves ahead toward dhyāna (meditation) and samādhi (absorption), the sublime states of yoga.

gītādhyayanaśīlasya prāṇāyāmaparasya ca /
naiva santi hi pāpāni pūrvajanmakṛtāni ca //

"By studying the sacred text Gītā and by practising prāṇāyāma regularly the evil impressions (sins) of the previous birth accumulated in the mind are destroyed".

By yogāsanas we correct the disorders of the gross body. Prāṇāyāma impacts the subtle body more than the yogāsanas, and it is not only the subtle body but also the gross body that is directly and obviously influenced by prāṇāyāma. Lungs, heart and brain play a very important role in our body, and the healthiness of these three is intimately linked with one another.

Broadly speaking, prāṇāyāma is a procedure of the exercise of inhaling and exhaling which makes the lungs strong, and gets the benefit of overall health and long life with the improvement in blood circulation. According to physiology, both the lungs in human beings are the apparatuses of inhaling, and the air inhaled in them gives oxygen to the whole body, and throws the carbonic gas out of various organs. If this action goes on properly, the lungs get strong and blood continues to be purified.

Generally most people are not used to breathing deeply. As a result, only about a quarter part of the lungs functions and the remaining three quarters remain almost idle. Like a honeycomb (beehive) the lungs have about 7,30,00,000 sponge-like cells (alveoli). In normal light breathing the prāṇa-vāyu circulates in about 20 million alveoli, the rest 53 million of them remain idle for want of circulation of prāṇa-vāyu. As a result they develop inertia and impurities and foreign matter starts depositing in them, and a person falls prey to deadly diseases, like tuberculosis, cough, bronchitis, etc.

Thus, the incomplete (fractional) activity of lungs influences the purification and circulation of blood. Mental disorders like agitation, anxiety, despondency, anger, fear, lasciviousness, etc. can be successfully treated with prāṇāyāma. Along with mental efficiency one can improve one's memory, sharpness, common sense, farsightedness, minute observation, concentration, intellect, etc. through prāṇāyāma, and thereby enjoy a long and really happy life.

Thus, prāṇāyāma becomes extremely important for the longevity of a person. Various diseases can be warded off easily by regulating the prāṇa-vāyu through prāṇāyāma. With the knowledge of this science, i.e. the science of prāṇa-vāyu, a person can regulate his own health as well as of others and can increase his longevity by benefitting fully from a happy and blissful life. That is why our age-old religion includes prāṇāyāma as an essential ritual on auspicious occasions and in the morning-evening meditative prayers.

By doing prāṇāyāma we start breathing long and deep instinctively. In the life granted us by God, we have been given counted number of breaths or prāṇas. A person gets his next birth according to his deeds.

sati mūle tadvipāko jātyāyurbhogāḥ.

(YOGADARŚANA: 2.13)

As a result of his meritorious or non-meritorious deeds a person qualifies for his birth as a human being, an animal, an insect, etc., for his longevity, for his enjoyments. One who practices prāṇāyāma uses fewer breaths, and has therefore a long life. Otherwise also, in this universe the creatures taking fewer breaths live proportionately longer.

The speed of breathing of a creature is a determining factor in its longevity, which is quite obvious to us. A turtle normally takes 4-5 breaths in a minute and it lives for 200-400 years. A human being normally takes 12-18 breaths, averaging 16 breaths in a minute. In the course of gaining control of breath through prāṇāyāma, although in bhastrikā, kapālabhāti, anuloma- viloma, etc. the number of breaths gets fewer or more at the time of prāṇāyāma, but after prāṇāyāma, all the day long there is a rhythm and stability in breaths. Therefore, in the earlier stage a yoga practitioner starts breathing 8-10 times per minute, which after a long practice comes down to 4-6 per minute. When a normal person takes 16 breaths per minute on an average, his average longevity is about 100 years. A normal person takes 23,040 (roughly 24,000) breaths in one day in 24 hours, whereas a yogi takes. 6000 breaths in one day (24 hours). When with the normal 16 breaths per minute a person lives for 100 years, the full longevity of a yoga practitioner with his breathing rate of 4 per minute goes up to 400 years. According to scriptures and seers-sages, the maximum life- span of a man is 400 years. In the beginning the practitioner of yoga takes 8 breaths per minute which comes down to 4 with the regular practice of prāṇāyāma and meditation. Therefore, a yogi can achieve the long life of 400 years. This is the secret of the longevity of ṛsis. As the Manusmṛti says:

ṛṣayo dīrghasandhyatvād dīrghamāyuravāpnuyuḥ /
prajñāṁ yaśaśca kīrtiṁ ca brahmavarcasameva ca //

"Ṛṣis achieved a long life by doing sandhyā (proper meditation) for long hours daily. Along with this they were also able to achieve intellect, fame, glory and divine radiance (brahmateja)."

How beautiful is this observation in Caraka Saṁhitā on the greatness of prāṇa:

vayustantrayantradharaḥ, pravartakaścesṭānāmuccāva-cānāṁ,
niyantā praṇetā ca manasaḥ, sarvendriyāṇāmudyojakaḥ,
sarvendriyārthānāmabhivoḍha ayuṣo 'nuvṛttiprat- yayabhūtaḥ //
(CARAKASAṀHITĀ)

"Air (vāyu) is the holder of this body-machine; it is the propeller of all its activities. It is the controller of the mind straying towards undesirable things, and is the motivator of the mind for desirable things. It is also the motivator of all sense organs. It connects all the sense organs to the mind and is witness to the continuity of life."

vāyurāyurbalaṁ vāyurvāyurdhātā śarīriṇām /
vāyurviśvamidaṁ sarvaṁ prabhurvāyuśca kīrtitaḥ //
(CARAKASAṀHITĀ)

"Air is life, air is strength, air is the sustainer of living beings, air is the cause of this universe, and air has been called the lord of all."

śarīraṁ hi vinā vāyuṁ samatāṁ yāti dārubhiḥ/
vāyuḥ prāṇaḥ sukhaṁ vāyurvāyuḥ sarvamidaṁ jagat //
(RĀMĀYAṆA)

"The body without air is like faggots (insentient). Therefore air is the prāṇa (life) in the body; in short, it is every thing."

yena jīvati jīvo 'yaṁ nirjīvo yaṁ nirjīvo yaṁ vinā bhavet /

sa prāṇa iti vikhyāto vāyuḥ kṣetracaraḥ paraḥ //

(ŚARṄGADHARAPADDHATI)

"What keeps a living being alive, without which the body become lifeless, that is called 'praṇa'. This prāṇa-vāyu (vital air) is the best of all that roam in the body (kṣetra)."

prāṇo brahmeti vyajānāt.
prāṇāddhyeva khalvimāni bhūtāni jāyante, prāṇena jātāni jīvanti prāṇaṁ prayantyabhisaṁviśanti.

(TAITTIRĪYOPANIṢAD 3.3)

"Living beings are born of prāṇa, on being born they are kept alive by prāṇa, and in the end dissolve into prāṇa."

prāṇaṁ devā anuprāṇanti manuṣyāḥ paśavaśca ye /
prāṇo hi bhūtānāmāyustasmātsarvāyuṣamucyate //

(TAITTIRĪYA UP. 2.3)

"Gods, human beings, birds and animals become the followers of prāṇa and perform prāṇana (keep body and soul together). Therefore, he is called 'sarvāyuṣa' (the life of all)."

sarvameva ta āyuryānti ye prāṇaṁ brahmopāsate /
prāṇo hi bhūtānāmāyustasmātsarvāyuṣamucyate //

(TAITTIRĪYA UP. 2.3)

"Those who worship prāṇa as 'brahma' attain full longevity. Prāṇa only is the age of living beings. That is why it is called 'sarvāyuṣa'."

ātharvaṇīrāṅgirasīrdaivī manuṣyajā uta /
oṣadhayaḥ prajāyante yadā tvaṁ prāṇa jinvasi //

(ATHARVAVEDA 11.4.16)

"O Prāṇa! The ātharvaṇī, āṅgirasī, divine and man-made medicines are efficacious only till you inhabit the body propelling it."

prāṇāyāmena yuktena sarvarogakṣayo bhavet /
ayuktābhyāsayogena sarvarogasya saṁbhavaḥ //

(HAṬHAYOGAPRADĪPIKĀ)

"With the prāṇāyāma done methodically all the diseases are eradicated, and all diseases can develop by doing the prāṇāyāma in an improper way."

pavano badhyate yena manastenaiva badhyate /
manaśca badhyate yena pavanastena badhyate //

(HATHAYOGAPRADĪPIKĀ)

"The means by which air (vāyu) is restrained also restrains the mind, and the means by which the mind is restrained also restrains the air."

The reward of Prāṇa-worship

> **yathā prāṇa balihṛtastubhyaṁ sarvaḥ prajā imāḥ /**
> **evā tasmai baliṁ harānyastvā śṛṇavat suśravaḥ /**
> **(ATHARVA. 11.4.19)**

prāṇa yathā = O Praṇa, as
imāḥ sarvāḥ prajāḥ = all these subjects
tubhyaṁ = unto you
balihṛtaḥ = are tax (tribute)-payers
evā = similarly
suśravaḥ = the noble listener
yaḥ tvā śṛṇavat = who listens to you
tasmai balim harān = to him you pay the tax (tribute)

'Prāṇa' means life-prop. When the soul comes into the body, the prāṇas also come and settle there. With the prāṇa going in and out, one feels the existence of soul in the body. If the soul departs from the body, prāṇas also do not stay there. The soul is nonphysical; its hunger cannot be satisfied by physical substances. Then the things that we eat and drink, take the tax from earth in the form of foodgrains, fruit, nuts, etc., drink water, milk, etc., keep ourselves cosy and comfortable with fire and blankets–for whom are we doing all this? The Vedas have an answer–

> **prāṇa balihṛtastubhyaṁ sarvāḥ prajā imāḥ.**

'O Prāṇa! Fire-air-water–all these subjects are paying you tax (tribute)."

Its proof lies in the fact that by eating and drinking the body is nourished and the sense organs become strong. The life-force (prāṇa-śakti) is strengthened. There is no growth or decay of the soul by eating or not eating. Had eating and drinking been the cause of growth and decay of the soul, then all the gluttons would have been spiritually advanced; but these gluttons go the demoniac way of life of eating, drinking and being merry. Therefore, eating and drinking is, in fact, for the sake of prāṇa. When the vital air (prāṇa-vāyu) and the gastric fire combine to sap the strength of tissues in our body, the we feel hungry, and we have to satisfy our hunger by taking food, etc. similarly, when they combine to dry up water in the body, then we feel thirsty, and to quench our thirst we have to take water. Food and water is the tax paid to prāṇa.

But the function of prāṇa is not merely to consume food and water, to metabolise it, and to demand it again. On close scrutiny, we shall find that when we eat or drink, the prāṇa stops, our trachea is closed. If the trachea remains open at that time, food and water goes into it, causing great discomfort which continues until the food or water gone into the trachea is not cleared out. This proves that on one hand prāṇa is the prop for life, while on the other it is very essential to restrain prāṇas for the sake of life. If the activity of prāṇa is not restrained, prāṇa cannot have its due.

While lifting some weight from the ground prāṇas have to be compulsively restrained. If the prāṇas (breath) give way/exit at that time, the weight falls down from our hands. This shows that there is great force in prāṇa-restraint.

Perhaps, that is why Manu says:

prāṇāyāmaḥ paraṁ tapaḥ-There is no greater penance than prāṇāyāma.

One who listens to these and this type of mysteries of prāṇa is 'suśravaḥ'. The listening of only that person is fruitful who acquires the knowledge of these powers of prāṇa.

tasmai baliṁ harān-Even prāṇas pay the tax to him.

Only they pay taxes (tributes) who are subordinate to somebody, i.e., prāṇa becomes their subordinate who after attaining knowledge conduct themselves accordingly. Therefore, to gain control of prāṇa one should do prāṇāyāma. Even while gaining control of prāṇa one has to run the prāṇas like bellows.

Therefore, Manu Says:

prāṇāyāmairdahed doṣan

One should destroy physical and mental flaws by prāṇāyāma.

Knowledge through prāṇa

vīḷu cidārujatnubhirguhā cidindra vahnibhiḥ /
avinda usriyā anu // **(ṚG. 1.6.5)**

Meaning-**indra** O embodied soul! **ārujatnubhiḥ** torturing, tiring **vahnibhiḥ** by prāṇas, the cause of holding life **guhā cit** even though hidden **usriyā** rays of knowledge **vīḷu cit** quickly **anu avindah** acquires appropriately, smoothly.

Interpretation:-The importance of prāṇa has been described in a few words. Here, instead of prāṇa, it has been called 'vahni'. In classical Sanskrit the word 'vahni' means 'fire'.

The fire of life burns in the body only till the prāṇas dwell in it. The moment prāṇas depart the body also becomes cold and lifeless. Therefore, prāṇa is really fire. If fire gives us comfort, it gives us pain too. The experience of the pain from fire is fully felt in the summer season. Every thing gets parehed and dried up. Similarly, when the prāna-fire does not get the fuel, it starts burning up the flesh and blood in the body, but the pain-giving aspect of prāṇas is fully realized when one lies on the death-bed. The enjoyment stage is over. The fire of death (yama) has arrived to snatch the life-bird from the cage of body. The passage for prāṇa is blocked. It is not getting any way out; it is straining at the cage bars and writhing in pain. Looking at this miserable plight of the dying person, the seeker of liberation (mumukṣu) gains control over these pain-giving prāṇas. Seeing that the time of death has arrived he pulls these prāṇas out easily and expels them.

He does not let the prāṇas be fire (a burning agent) but makes them the fire (vahni=holder, carrier) of the Vedas. Now the prāṇas have been made 'vahni', they have been held; their movement has been stopped; therefore, they have also become holders. In this respect, prāṇa and dharma (the path of righteous conduct) behave in the same way. Dharma kills if it is killed (=not properly observed), and it protects if properly observed. Prāṇa, if converted into fire, burns, but in the form of vahni (holder, carrier) it enlivens. The choice is yours whether you want to live or to burn.

Even after being converted into 'vahni', the prāṇa continues to be 'ārujatnu' (destroyer, demolisher). Now it does not break limbs, does not torture the body, because with the help of prāṇic procedures the body has been purged of all its dross. Now it rips apart the screen of ignorance covering the soul. Therefore the Veda says: **avinda usriyā anu**-O Soul! It is you who receive the rays of knowledge smoothly.

The great yogi Patañjali has confirmed this truth of the Veda on the basis of his experience: **tataḥ kṣīyate prakāśāvaraṇam (YOGADARŚANA)**– with the perfecting of prāṇāyāma the screen (haze) covering the light of intellect is destroyed.

The Veda says further–

yadā gacchātyasunītimetāmathā devānāṁ vaśanīrbhavati.
(ṚG. 10.16.2)

"When the seeker acquires 'asunīti' (the discipline of propelling prāṇas), then he becomes the controller of sense organs."

If you want to control sense organs, control the prāṇa. There is a lot of profundity in this statement. The sense organs are dominated by the mind. The mind is very unstable, very quick–it is the quickest of all. The sense organs follow it wherever it goes. The controlling of sense organs by 'asunīti' (praṇic discipline) means also the controlling of the mind, the supreme lord of sense organs. This state is called 'yoga'. As the Kaṭhopaniṣad says:

yadā pañcāvatiṣthante jñānāni manasā saha /
buddhiśca na viceṣṭati tāmāhuḥ paramāṁ gatim //
tāṁ yogamiti manyante sthirāmindriyadhāraṇām //
(2.3.10-11)

"When all the five senses of perception are restrained along with the mind, and the intellect also becomes unwavering, that state is called 'paramagati' (supreme state). That stabilized concentration of the senses is called 'yoga'. Practise prāṇāyāma if you want to control the senses, or if you want to put your senses to their proper use. Attain perfection in prāṇāyāma if you want to rip off the screen of ignorance from your intellect and want to achieve the pure, radiant and white light of knowledge."

The great savant of prāṇāyāma, Swami Dayanand, says in the third chapter of Satyarthaprakāśa: "When a person practises prāṇāyāma, then every moment progressively he destroys impurity and illumines the light of knowledge. The knowledge of his soul goes on increaseing till he attains liberation. As the dross in metals like gold, etc. is destroyed on their being heated in fire and they get purified, similarly with the practice of prāṇāyāma the flaws and impurities in the mind and senses are destroyed and they become pure....By gaining control over prāṇas one gains control over the mind and senses. There is an increase in strength and prowess, and the intellect becomes so sharp and subtle that it grasps quickly very difficult and abstruse topics. This increases semen in a man's body and he gains firm strength, valour and conquest over his senses. He masters all the scriptures in a short time and they are always on his tongue. Women should also practise yoga likewise."

The Vedas, Manu, Patañjali, Dayanand–all sing the glory of prāṇa unanimously.

The protector of prāṇas remains protected altogether–

> **na sa jīyate maruto na hanyate na sredhati na vyathate na riṣyati /**
> **nāsya rāya upa dasyanti notaya ṛṣiṁ vā yaṁ rājānaṁ vā suṣūdatha //** **(ṚG. 5.54.7)**

Meaning : **marutaḥ** O Prāṇas! **yaṁ** whom **ṛṣiṁ** to the savant **vā** or **rājānam** one engaged in the duty of protecting others **vā** or some other person **suṣūdatha** provide comfort, happiness, **saḥ** he **na** not **jīyate** put to any harm or loss, **na** not **sredhati** lose his longevity **na+vyathate** does not tremble with fear **na+riṣyati** does not become angry, **na** nor (does) **asya** his **rāyaḥ** wealth **upadasyanti** decay and **na** nor do his **ūtayaḥ** affections, affinities, good relations perish.

Interpretation: A man is haunted by many fears, sometimes of the loss in his longevity, sometimes of death, sometimes of being humiliated or reprimanded by somebody, sometimes one develops tremors or shivering in body due to some disease, sometimes he is tormented by the fear of losing his wealth, and sometimes the fear of losing his good and cordial relations worries him a lot. The Vedas say that if you want to get rid of all these tensions, seek the refuge of prāṇa. If you are able to engage/deploy prāṇas for your security, you will not be agitated by any fear.

All agree that you live a longer life with the practice of prāṇa. Therefore, whoever disciplines his prāṇas, will live longer, not shorter. One does not suffer the affliction of death if one disciplines the prāṇa. Death is a certainty. Whoever is born will definitely die–**jātasya hi dhruvo mṛtyuḥ.** The death of one who is born is inevitable, but one who practises prāṇa is saved of the torturing pain felt by a dying person (mumūrṣu) on his death-bed. Being face to face with death he immediately expels his prāṇa without much effort immediately. With the disciplining of prāṇa he achieves self-realization, and he feels that the soul as that of his dwells in everybody, which makes him eschew violence and anger. One gets angry on account of somebody's faults and mistakes. The disciplining of prāṇas has made him realize his own faults and shortcomings; now he gets busy with correcting his own faults. He has no time to find faults in others. His eyes are still looking for faults, but for his own faults, and not of others. One is haunted by fear or trembling at the prospect of losing some thing or substance. When that possibility exists no more, where is the cause for any fear or worry?

The wealth of such an ascetic (abstemious person) never decays because he disciplines prāṇas and observes abstinence in his life strictly; he has guarded himself against all evil addictions. By virtue of self-realization, he behaves himself wisely and sagaciously with love and affection toward everybody. Therefore, he is loved by one and all.

> **pra nū sa martaḥ śavasā janāṁ ati tasthau va ūtī maruto yamāvata. (RG. 1.64.13)**

"O Prāṇas! That man is really superior in strength to the common people whom you give your loving protection."

There is great strength/power in prāṇa. While lifting any weight from the ground if the breath gives way in between, the weight falls down from the hand, because prāṇa, the prop of strength, went out. Therefore, those who desire to build up strength in their body must practise prāṇāyāma.

Rarely anybody pays heed to prāṇas-

> **yaddha yānti marutaḥ saṁ ha bruvate 'dhvannā /**
> **śṛṇoti kaścideṣām // (ṚG. 1.37.13)**

Meaning : **yat + ha** whenever **marutaḥ** prāṇas **yānti** move **ha** really **adhvan** on the way **ā** all around **saṁ + bruvate** tell clearly. **kaścit** rarely anybody **eṣaṁ** (words) of these **prāṇas śṛnoti** listens, pays heed to.

Interpretation : This universe is a storehouse of strange things. The microcosm, that our body seems, is also a sort of museum. The eyes, nose, ears, etc. in the body are attracted to certain things. The eyes are thirsting for beauty, the ears are hungry for sound, the tongue wants palatable things, the nose loves fragrant flowers, the skin is itching for contact. The beauty, etc. allure the eyes and deviate them from the right path; but prāṇas are not enamoured of any thing. Even unparalleled beauty, most melodious words, ambrosial food and drinks, feather-soft touch and heavenly perfume cannot create any hindrance in its work. Yajurveda puts it very beautifully: **tatra jāgṛto**

asvapnajau satrasadau ca devau. In that body the gods running the yajña of life are never overcome by sleep and keep an incessant vigil. The eye blinks, and shuts. The tongue also gets fed up. Similarly fatigue overtakes all the sense organs, but the prāṇas are ever awake. They are very dutiful sentinels. They are so very beneficence-minded that-**yaddha yānti marutaḥ saṁ ha bruvate 'dhvannā**-when they move/circulate they go on announcing their full route.

Observe an infant while he is sleeping; whither to whither are his breaths (prāṇas) going. They are clearly going up to the navel and come back upward from there. Put your hand on the fontanelle of the infant; on that very tender spot there, put your hand very carefully and delicately. You will feel the strong stroke of prāṇa there. In this way prāṇas are telling you their route: "Our route runs from the bottom upward." Arrange so that the prāṇas reach upward. Prāṇas are always on the move. Therefore, they are always transmitting their message; but–**śṛnoti kascideṣām**–rarely anybody listens to them. Whoever listens to them, he becomes capable of controlling his senses–**ni vo yāyāma mānuṣo dadha ugrāya manyave/ jihīta parvato giriḥ** (ṚG 1.37.7). If a human being prevents you from your extreme (volatile) thinking even for three hours, even the mountain (made of many strata of rocks) feels the tremor. Listen to the prāṇas for a couple of hours, control them, hold them, your internal mountain-ranges (spine) will also feel the tremor. Suṣumṇā (spinal cord) will wake up. To put in a few words, even the duration of time was laid down for awakening suṣumṇā. Sitting unmoved for three hours (one prahara) with restratined breath (prāṇa) awakens suṣumṇā. Experienced seekers confirm it on the basis of their own experience.

Two airs (vāyus) (prāṇa-apāna)–

> **dvāvimau vātau vāta ā sindhorā parāvataḥ /**
> **dakṣaṁ te anya ā vātu parā 'nyo vātu yadrapaḥ //**
>
> **(ṚG. 10.137.2)**

In our body (dvau imau vātau) two types of air, prāṇa and apāna (vātaḥ) are moving. One out of these two (ā+parāvataḥ) is up to the outer atmosphere. O Prāṇāyāma - practising man! one out of them, i.e. prāṇa-vāyu, (te) in you (dakṣam) health, vigour, courage and vitality (āvātu) may bring, instil and (anyaḥ) the other one i.e. apāna-vāyu (yadrapaḥ) whatever debility and diseases are in you, them (parā vātu) may throw out of the body.

Conquering sins with the help of prāṇa–

vṛtrasya tvā śvasathādīṣamāṇā viśve devā ajahurye sakhāyaḥ / marudbhirindra sakhyaṁ te astvathemā viśvāḥ pṛtanā jayāsi //

(ṚG. 8.96.7)

viśve devāḥ = all divine attributes
ye sakhāyaḥ= which were friends earlier
vṛtrasya śvasathāt= by the breath of sin
īṣamāṇāḥ= being frightened
tvām ajahuḥ= deserted you
indra= (therefore) O Indra, opulence-desiring person
marudbhiḥ= with Maruts (Prāṇas)
te sakhyaṁ astu= may be your friendship
atha= so that
imaḥ viśvāḥ= all these
pṛtanāḥ= tensions and worries
jayāsi= you may conquer.

The Soul has many divine attributes, like compassion, pardon, fortitude, purity, restraint, non-violence, truthfulness, control, etc. These attributes go on growing constantly till the sin makes its entry into the Soul. The quartet of dharma (righteous conduct), artha (wealth), kāma (sex, desire) and mokṣa (liberation) also dwells in the Soul amicably. All four–**guṇānurāgādiva sakhyamīyivān–**are as if in mutual friendship due to their affinity with attributes. There is a constant war between the gods and Vṛtra. 'Vṛtra' means overcasting sin. The sin is hostile to good attributes.

The good attributes try to put the sin to rout. Thus a duel fight with the Soul starts. When the Soul becomes more inclined toward Vṛtra, then frightened by the camping in Vṛtra-

viśve devā ajahurye sakhāyaḥ

"All divine attributes which were earlier friends of the Soul desert company."

With the growth of sin all gods (divine attributes) disappear. What will remain of the Soul after the disappearance of divine attributes? If the Soul and divine attributes are to be protected, put the sins to rout. For vanquishing the sins, **'marudbhirindra sakhyaṁ te astu'**- 'O Indra! you should develop friendship with prāṇas' means that the prāṇas move in consonance with the Soul. At present, the layman has no knowledge of the movement of his inhalation and exhalation. The breath goes in and out in accordance with divine dispensation. They are no doubt incarcerated in the body due to the Soul dwelling in the body, but they do not move in consonance with the Soul. If the prāṇas move in consonance with the Soul, there shall never be any disease in the body. If the prāṇas be under the control of the Soul, the mind and sense organs will also be under the control of the Soul. If the mind is controlled, sense organs will automatically be controlled, because they are under the subjugation of the mind. It is proved by experience that by gaining control over prāṇa (vital air) the mind is also controlled. Therefore, the Vedas say: **athemā viśvāḥ pṛtanā jayāsi**– 'you will be able to conquer all these tensions and worries.' All the tensions and agitations which are born of sin can be destroyed by developing friendship and consonance with prāṇa. The underlying reason is : **prāṇaya namo yasya sarvamidaṁ vaśe** : 'obeisance to Prāṇa who controls this all.' What doubt can there be in the prāṇa being the lord of all? Therefore, we should develop friendship with this sovereign lord, i.e., Prāṇa.

The friendship with Prāṇa develops with the practice of prāṇāyāma. Harm is caused by not doing prāṇāyāma, by not restraining prāṇas. As the Atharvaveda says:

sa ya evaṁ viduṣa upadraṣṭā bhavati prāṇaṁ ruṇaddhi // 54 // na ca prāṇaṁ sarvajyāniṁ jīyate purainaṁ jarasaḥ prāṇo jahāti // 56 //

"One who is the disciple of the savant attaining brahmajñāna (knowledge of the Supreme), performs the control / restraint of prāṇa (prāṇāyāma). If he does not perform prāṇa-restraint (prānāyām), he incurs loss of his whole life. If not the loss of his life, prāṇa deserts him before old age."

This statement proves that a man suffers loss by not doing prāṇāyāma. It is not possible to conserve semen in the body without prāṇāyāma. Semen is the essence of life; it is the prop of life. The basis of this life-support in prāṇāyāma is extremely essential for a long life. The description of prāṇa given in the Vedas proves that the meaning of prāṇāyāma is to control prāṇa (life-force). While the controlling of this life-force contributes to your longevity, there is no torment at the time of death. Finding oneself face to face with death the Soul expels the prāṇas without any effort. Such a great soul is called 'mṛtyuñjaya' (conqueror of death).

We have told it a number of times that sin is destroyed with the practice of prāṇāyāma. The Soul has to face many types of agitations and tensions. The activity of life depends on prāṇa, this has also been said in the preceding mantra. If the prāṇic activity is not going in the proper way, a person falls prey to a host of diseases, like cough, cold, asthma, tuberculosis, etc. Therefore, it is most essential to control the prāṇas for protecting the body against diseases. There is an intimate relationship between the prāṇa and the mind. The restraining of prāṇa is indispensable for removing the unstability of the mind. The relation between the Soul and the prāṇa is obvious. Prāṇas cannot stay in the body without the soul, and there is no incontrovertible proof of the existence of soul in the body in the absence of movement of prāṇas therein. For making the extrovert Soul introvert, along with the mind and sense organs, for realizing one's self, the restraining/controlling of prāṇa is the best means. From this point of view it is proved that it is most beneficial to gain control over the prāṇa to dispel physical and mental blemishes. Therefore, the Vedas say:

It is very logical-**'marudbhirindra sakhyaṁ te astvathemā viśvāḥ pṛtanā jayāsi.'**

Bṛhadviṣṇu :

> **prāṇāyāmān dvijaḥ kuryāt sarvapāpānupattaye /**
> **dahyante sarvapāpāni prāṇāyāmairdvijasya tu //**

"A seeker should do prāṇāyāma to dispel all sins. By doing prāṇāyāma all sins are burnt, are destroyed."

Viṣṇudharmottarapurāṇāgnipurāṇa :

> **sarvadoṣaharaḥ proktaḥ prāṇāyāmo dvijanmanām /**
> **tatastvabhyadhikaṁ nāsti pāpanāśanakāraṇam //**

"For the twice-born prāṇāyāma has been called the destroyer of all flaws and blemishes. There is no greater agent than this to destroy sins."

Atri:

> **karmaṇā manasā vācā hyahnā pāpaṁ kṛtaṁca yat /**
> **āsīnaḥ paścimāṁ sandhyāṁ prāṇāyāmairvyapohati //**

"Whatever sins of mind, speech and action are committed by a person during the day are dispelled by him by doing prāṇāyāma in the evening twilight."

Agnipurāna :

prāṇāyāmatrayaṁ kṛtvā prāṇāyāmāistribhirniśi /
ahorātrakṛtāt pāpāt mucyate nātra saṁśayaḥ //

"By doing three prāṇāyāmas each in the morning and evening, a man is emancipated of the sins committed by him during day and night."

Vasiṣṭha :

prāṇāyāmān dhārayet trīn yathāvidhi suyantritaḥ /
ahorātrakṛtaṁ pāpaṁ tatkṣaṇādeva naśyati //
(prāṇāyāmairdahed doṣān prāṇāyāmaḥ paraṁ tapaḥ)

"One should do three prāṇāyāmas everyday methodically and with proper restraint. With this a person is liberated of the sins committed by him during day and night."

Bṛhaspati:

prāṇāyāmairdahed doṣān manovāgdehasaṁbhavān.

"By prāṇāyāmā one should destroy the sins of mind, speech and body."

Baudhāyana :

etadādyaṁ tapaḥ proktametaddharmasya lakṣaṇam /
sarvadoṣopaghātārthametadeva viśiṣyate //

"This (prāṇāyāma) has been called the main penance. It is a sign of dharma (righteous conduct). It has been considered to be a special means for destroying all the sins and blemishes."

Atri and Vasiṣtha:

āvarttayet sadā yuktaḥ prāṇāyāmān punaḥ punaḥ /
ākeśāgrānnakhāgrācca tapastapyata uttamam //

"A mam should always concentrate his mind and repeat prāṇāyāmas again and again. One who does this performs the supreme penance from top to toe."

Viṣṇudharmottara-Agnipurāṇa:

ākeśāgrānnakhāgrācca tapastapyet sudāruṇam /
ātmānaṁ śodhayatyeva prāṇāyāmaḥ punaḥ punaḥ //

"One who does prāṇāyāma does a hard penance from top to toe. The prāṇāyāma done repeatedly purifies a man."

Bṛhadyama:

yathā hi śailadhātūnāṁ dhamyatāṁ dhamyate rajaḥ /
indriyaṇāṁ tathā doṣān prāṇāyāmaiśca nirdahet //

"As the dross of metals taken from a mountain is removed by blasts of air in fire, similarly a person should burn away the faults and blemishes of sense organs by doing prāṇāyāma."

Bṛhaspati: Vācaspatyam-p.4516

dhamyamānaṁ yathā hyetaddhātūnāṁ dhamyate malam /
tathendriyakṛto doṣaḥ prāṇāyāmena dahyate //

"As the dross of metals is destroyed by blasts of air in fire, similarly the faults of sense organs are burnt away by prāṇāyāma."

Yogiyājñavalkya:

yathā parvatadhātūnāṁ doṣān dahati pāvakah /
evamantargatam calnam prāṇāyāmena dahyate //

"As the fire burns away the dross of metals of the mountain, similarly internal dross and sins are burnt away by prāṇāyāma."

Atri and Vasiṣṭha :

nirodhājjāyate vāyurvāyoragniḥ prajāyate /
agnerāpo vyajāyanta tairantaḥ śudhyati tribhiḥ //

"By holding up the breaths (prāṇas) with prāṇāyama, air accumulates in the body. This generates fire and heat in the body and after this there is water or perspiration. Thus by doing three prāṇāyāmas there is internal cleansing by air, fire and water. The body and the mind become clean."

Viṣṇudharmottara-Agnipurāṇa :

nirodhājjāyate vāyustasmādagnistato jalam /
tribhiḥ śarīraṁ sakalaṁ prāṇāyāmairviśudhyati //

Manu:

prāṇāyāmā brāhmaṇasya trayo 'pi vidhivatkṛtāh /
vyāhṛtipraṇavairyuktā vijñeyaṁ paramaṁ tapaḥ //

(MANUSMṚTI 6.70)

"If a person does even three prāṇāyāmas in the proper method chanting in his mind 'oṁ bhūrbhuvaḥ svaḥ." i.e. oṁkāra with the three mystical incantations, it is the supreme penance for him. Three is the minimum number prescribed. A person is benefitted more if he does it more according to his practice and capacity."

Yogacūḍāmaṇi Upaniṣad :

prāṇāyāmo bhavedevaṁ pātakendhanapāvakaḥ /
bhavodadhimahāsetuḥ procyate yogibhiḥ sadā //

Prāṇāyāma is the fire which burns down the faggots of sin; it is the great bridge to go across the ocean of mundane existence,–this is what the yogis say.

yuktaṁ yuktaṁ tyajedvāyum yuktaṁ yuktaṁ prapūrayet /
yuktaṁ yuktaṁ prabadhnīyādevaṁ siddhimavāpnuyāt //

"A prāṇāyāma- practitioner should exhale and inhale in the proper manner and also hold it inside according to his capacity in the proper manner. Thus, by doing the prāṇāyāma cautiously and methodically, one achieves success."

Manu:

prāṇāyāmairdahed doṣān dhāraṇābhiśca kilviṣam /
pratyāhāreṇa saṁsargān dhyānenānīśvarān guṇān //
(MANUSMṚTI 6.72)

"By prāṇayāmas a man should burn down evils, like rāga (attachment) etc. By dhāraṇā (concentration) he should destroy sins, by pratyāhāra (withdrawal) he should ward off the attraction of sense organs for various enjoyments, and by dhyāna (meditation)"....

ahnā rātryā ca yān jantūn hinastvajñānato yatiḥ /
teṣāṁ snātvā viśuddhyarthaṁ prāṇāyāmān ṣaḍāearet //
(MANUSMṚTI 6.69)

"While walking around during day and night one kills insects, worms, etc. For the purification of this sin an ascetic should do six prāṇāyāmas after taking bath."

ekākṣaraṁ paraṁ brahma prāṇāyāmaḥ paraṁ tapaḥ /
sāvitryāstu paraṁ nāsti maunāt satyaṁ viśiṣyate /
(MANUSMṚTI 2.83)

"The single syllable 'oṁ' denotes the Supreme Brahman, or it is the real name of īśvara. Prāṇāyāma is the greatest penance. There is no mantra greater than Sāvitrī (Gāyatrī) Mantra. It is better to speak the truth than remain silent."

Aruṇasmṛti-p.2130

athavā mucyate pāpāt prāṇāyāmaparāyaṇah /
prāṇāyāmairdahet sarvaṁ śarīre yacca pātakam // 21 //

"One who does prāṇāyāma is liberated from sins. Therefore, all the dross, faults and blemishes in the body should be burnt down by prāṇāyāma."

yatha vegagato vahniḥ śuṣkārdraṁ dahatīndhanam /
prāṇāyāmaistathā pāpam śuṣkārdraṁ nātra saṁśayaḥ // 30 //

"The strong fire burns down all the fuel, dry or wet. Similarly, prāṇāyāma burns down big and small flaws and blemishes there is no doubt about it."

Bṛhadyogiyājñavalkyasmṛti:
Gāyatrī Prāṇāyāma
savyāhṛtiṁ sapraṇavāṁ gāyatrīṁ śirasā saha
triḥ paṭhedāyataprāṇaḥ prāṇāyāmaḥ sa ucyate

"Chant the Gāyatrī Mantra (along with OṀ BHŪRBHUVAḤ SVAḤ) three times in your mind while holding up your breath,– this (according to scriptures) is called prāṇāyāma, i.e., one prāṇāyāma is completed when you chant Gāyatrī Mantra thrice to yourself while holding the breath in or out.

Bṛhadyogiyājñavalkyasmṛti: 27-34 (P.2304)
prāṇāyāmaśataṁ kāryaṁ sarvapāpapraṇāśanam /
upapātakajātināmanādiṣṭasya caiva hi // BṚHA. 8.36 (p.2304)

"One hundred prāṇāyāmas should be done as an atonement for all the sins. By doing this no thought of committing any sin comes to the mind in future. The scriptures speak about upapātakas (minor sins); for their atonement also a person should do 100 prāṇāyāmas. This purifies the mind which turns away from committing any sin in future. A person should do 100 prāṇāyāmas as an atonement for those sins for which no atonement has been prescribed by the scriptures, so that one is not inclined again to commit those sins."

(Courtesy-SVĀDHYĀYA SANDOHA)

SOME RULES FOR PRĀṆĀYĀMA

- Prāṇāyāma should be done at a pure, calm and quiet and clean place. If possible, it should be practised near some body of water.
- In cities where there is a lot of pollution, the place before practising prāṇāyāma should be scented with ghee and guggulu (incense), or a lamp of ghee should be lit up
- For Prāṇāyāma one should sit in siddhāsana, sukhāsana or padmāsana with the spine held erect. The āsana used for sitting should be a bad conductor of electricity, e.g. a blanket or kuśa- mat. Those who are unable to sit on ground can practise prāṇāyāma while sitting in chair
- One should always breathe through nose. This filters the air during inhalation. Even during the day one should breathe through nose. This also regulates the temperature of the body through iḍā- piṅgalā nāḍīs and foreign matter stays out in the nostrils.
- While doing prāṇāyāma the mind should be calm and cheerful. Otherwise, through prāṇāyāma also the mind automatically becomes calm, cheerful and concentrated.
- If one feels tired while doing prāṇāyāma, one should do some light exercise (sūkṣma vyāyāma) or take rest in between.
- Do observe restraint and good conduct for the constant practice of prāṇāyāma. The food should be pure, simple and properly lubricating. It is beneficial to consume milk, ghee, almonds and fruit in right quantity.
- Do not hold the breath forcibly in prāṇāyāma. For doing prāṇāyāma, the act of breathing in is 'pūraka', holding it inside is 'kumbhaka', breathing out is 'recaka', and to hold the breath outside is 'bāhyakumbhaka'.
- Prāṇāyāma does not merely mean 'pūraka', 'kumbhaka' or 'recaka'; it also means practising to make the mind stable and concentrated while controlling and balancing the rate of breathing.

- It is spiritually beneficial that before prāṇāyāma one should do long chanting of 'OM' at least three times, or one should methodieally chant or recite Gāyatrī, Mahāmṛtyuñjaya or some other Vedic mantra.
- While doing prāṇāyāma, one should be in his normal, natural state without putting any sort of stress on the organs of his body like face, mouth, eyes, nose, etc. During the practice of prāṇāyāma, sit with your neck, spine, chest and waist erect; only then the practice will be methodical and beneficial.
- Prāṇāyāma should be done slowly with patience and caution, without any hurry.

yathā siṁho gajo vyāghro bhaved vaśyaḥ śanaiḥ śanaiḥ /
tathaiva vaśyate vāyuranyathā hanti sādhakam //

"The ferocious wild animals like lions, elephants and tigers are tamed gradually with great caution. If this is done in a hurry, these animals can attack us and do us harm. Similarly, prāṇa (breath) should be brought under control by increasing the practice of prāṇāyāma gradually, otherwise harm can be caused to a learner".

To reap full benefit from the practice of all types of prāṇāyāmas one should memorize this śloka from Gītā and follow it by repeating it to oneself:

yuktāhāravihārasya yuktaceṣṭasya karmasu /
yuktasvapnāvabodhasya yogo bhavati duḥkhahā //

"If a person eats properly and conducts his life properly, has a set routine for his worldly activities, has a fixed time to go to bed and to get up, only such a person can practise yoga; and by practising yoga he destroys his miseries, not other persons".

- Prāṇāyāma should be done with clean bowels after morning toilet. If somebody has constipation he should take the juice of āmalaka (gooseberry) and ghṛtakumāri (aloe vera) after dinner. This will prevent constipation.
- One feels more delighted, cheerful and purified if prāṇāyāma is done after taking bath. If one likes to take bath after prāṇāyāma, it can be taken after 10-15 minutes. One can take juice, sprouted grains or some other food, 10-15 minutes after prāṇāyāma in the morning.

- One should not take tea, coffee or other stimulants and intoxicants immediately after prāṇāyāma.
- It is a healthy habit to take milk, curd, buttermilk, fruit juice, green vegetable juice, and fruits like papaya, apple, guava, cherry, etc.
- After prāṇāyāma one should take sprouted grains, porridge or some local/indigenous easily digestible food. In the first instance, one should avoid eating paranthas, halwa and other breakfast, and if one has a craving for paranthas, a healthy person may take such heavy breakfast only once, or at the most twice, in a week. A sick person should abstain from taking heavy (fatty, fried) food.
- It is not proper to take the same type of breakfast everyday. For complete nourishment of the body one should programme one's breakfast during the week in such a way that one changes from sprouted grains to porridge, to milk, to fruit only, to juice or curd only, to buttermilk etc. on different days. This will give complete nourishment to the body and the breakfast will not be a boredom. Change is the law of life, and our preference too.
- The food of a yoga practitioner should be pure and simple (sāttvika). Take green vegetables in a large quantity, take less quantity of cereals, and take the pulses with husk. Eat what is seasonal (ṛtabḥuk), what is in a limited quantity (mitabhuk) and what suits your health (hitabhuk). Vegetarian food is the best, wholesome and scientific.
- On getting up in the morning, drinking water and washing the eyes with cold water is very beneficial for stomach and eyes.
- One must drink water once between breakfast and lunch, and in small quantities several times between lunch and dinner. This protects us against diseases of digestive system, urinary system, obesity, cholesterol, etc.
- Pregnant women should not do kapālabhāti, bāhya prāṇāyāma and agnisāra kriyā but they should do rest of the prāṇāyāmas and light (sūkṣma) exercises like butterfly āsana, etc. gently. During the menstrual period women should not do bāhya prāṇāyāma and difficult āsanas. They must do regularly light exercises and all other prāṇāyāmas, except bahya prāṇāyāma, even during

the menstrual period. Pregnant women should not do difficult āsanas like sarvāṅgāsana, halāsana, etc.

- Persons suffering from hypertension and heart disease must do all the prāṇāyāmas gently. Prāṇāyāma is the only remedy for them. The only precaution to be observed is that they should practise bhastrikā, kapālabhāti and anuloma-viloma etc. gently, without applying too much of force. Some ignoramuses misinform people by saying that patients of high B.P and heart disease should not do prāṇāyāma. This is total ignorance.
- Kapālabhāti prāṇāyāma should be done 4-6 months after any surgery. In the case of bye-pass and angioplasty in heart disease, one must practise anuloma-viloma, bhrāmarī, udgītha prāṇāyāma, light (sūkṣma) exercises and śavāsana, after one week only. This will bring them immediate relief and benefit.

THE THREE USEFUL BANDHAS (LOCKS) IN PRĀṆĀYĀMA

The energy which goes outward from our body while practising yogāsana and prāṇāyāma is stopped by us and turned inward by bandhas (locks). Bandha only means to tie, to stop. These bandhas (locks) are great aids to prāṇāyāma. Without bandhas, prāṇāyāmas are incomplete. These bandhas are described below in proper order.

Jālandhara -bandha

Sit erect in padmāsana or siddhāsana and fill the breath inside. Both the hands should rest on the knees. Bending the chin downwards and resting it on the throat pit is called Jālandhara- bandha. The gaze should be fixed between the eyebrows. The chest is to be stretched forward. This bandh keeps the nāḍi- network in the throat tied up (strong and tight)

Benefits

- The throat becomes sweet, melodious and attractive.
- With the closure of iḍā, piṅgalā nāḍīs due to contraction of throat the prāna enters into suṣumṇā (spinal cord).
- It is beneficial in all the diseases of throat. It is worth practising in diseases of thyroid, tonsils, etc.
- It awakens the viśuddhi cakra (carotid plexus).

Uḍḍīyāna- bandha

The procedure which raises, elevates the prāṇa and makes it enter into suṣumṇā (spinal cord) is called uḍḍīyāna - bandha. While standing rest the hands on both the knees in the normal natural way. Breathe out and let the stomach relax. Raise the chest a little upward while applying 'jālandhara- bandha'. Suck the stomach inward toward the spine, as much as you can. Breathe again and repeat the procedure. To begin with, three times is sufficient. Gradually practise more times. Similarly, practise this bandha in padmāsana or siddhāsana also. (Vide Illustration No. 1 at the outset of this book)

Benefits

- Cures all stomach ailments.

- Awakens prāṇas and cleanses maṇipūra- cakra (solar plexus)

Mūlabandha

Sitting in siddhāsana or padmāsana, apply bāhya or ābhyantara kumbhaka and stretch upward the anus and urinary organ. In this bandha the region below the navel is stretched upward. This bandha is easy to apply with the help of bāhya kumbhaka. Those who are well-versed in yogic practices apply this bandha as a normal posture for several hours. Long practice should be done under somebody's guidance.

Benefits

- Apāna vāyu moves upward and unites with prāṇa. Thus, this bandha awakens the mūlādhāra cakra (pelvic plexus) and is very helpful in the awakening of kuṇḍalinī (serpent power).
- This bandha is excellent in curing constipation and piles and for toning up the digestive system.
- It causes the upward movement (ūrdhvaretas) of semen and is therefore very important for celibacy.

Mahābandha

Applying all the three bandhas simultaneously while sitting in any meditative pose like padmāsana, etc., is called 'mahābandha'. All the aforesaid benefits can be obtained through it. All these three bandhas are applied in kumbhaka.

Benefits

- Prāṇa moves upward.
- The semen gets purified and strength increases.
- Mahābandha causes the union of iḍā, piṅgalā and suṣumṇā.

THE COMPLETE (Eight) PRĀṆĀYĀMAS

Although various procedures of prāṇāyāma are described in scriptures and each prāṇāyāma has its special significance, yet all the prāṇāyāmas cannot be practised daily. Therefore, with the grace of my preceptors and on the basis of my own experience, I have condensed within eight procedures the whole process of prāṇayama in a distinct scientific method and spiritual way. The benefits which accrue from the complete practice of this prāṇāyāma are briefly listed below:

- The three doṣas–vāta, pitta and kapha–become balanced.
- The digestive system becomes completely balanced and all stomach ailments are cured.
- All the diseases of heart, lungs and brain are cured.
- From the common disorders like obesity, diabetes, cholesterol, constipation, flatulence, acidity, respiratory troubles, allergy, migraine, blood pressure, kidney ailments, all sexual diseases of male and female, etc to the incurable diseases like cancer are cured.
- High immunity is developed.
- One can protect oneself from hereditary diabetes, heart disease, etc.
- It gives protection against falling and greying of hair, wrinkles on face, poor eyesight, weak memory, etc,. i.e., old age will be delayed and one will live longer.
- There will be radiance, glow, lustre and serenity on your face.
- Spiritual power (kuṇḍalinī jāgaraṇa) will be attained through purification, penetration and awakening of cakras (energy centres).
- With the mind getting very stabilized, serene, cheerful and enthusiastic, one will get rid of diseases like depression, etc.
- One will start going into dhyāna (meditation) automatically and one will develop the capacity of practising meditation for hours together.
- All the diseases of the gross and the subtle body and the flaws like lust, anger, greed, delusion, egoism, etc. are eradicated.

- Negative thinking is eliminated, and one who practises prāṇāyāma is always full of positive thinking, energy and self confidence.

First procedure : Bhastrikā Prāṇāyāma

Sitting in a convenient meditative pose and filling the breath inside up to diaphragm through both the nostrils and then breathing it out gently is called bhastrikā prāṇāyāma.

The noble resolution (śiva saṅkalpa) during bhastrikā

While filling the breath inside during bhastrikā prāṇāyāma one should think (resolve) in his mind whatever is noble and pure in the Universe, such as divine power, energy, sanctity, serenity and bliss, is instilling into my body along with prāṇa. I am getting suffused with divine powers. The prāṇāyāma done with this divine resolution is essentially beneficial.

The duration of bhastrikā

There should be inhalation of 2½ seconds and exhalation of 2½ seconds in a rhythmic flow. Thus by doing it non-stop, one can do bhastrikā prāṇāyāma 12 times in one minute. One should do it for 5 minutes in one sitting. In the beginning one may have to take rest in between. It takes about a week to develop the practice of this prāṇāyāma for 5 minutes non-stop.

Healthy persons and slightly sick persons should practise bhastrikā for 5 minutes daily. Those who are suffering from cancer, lung fibrosis, muscular dystrophy, MS, SLE and other incurable diseases should do this prāṇāyāma for 10 minutes. Thus bhastrikā is done 12 times in one minute and 60 times in 5 minutes. If done in two sittings in incurable diseases like cancer this prāṇyāma is best done 120 times. Normally prāṇāyāma is best done empty stomach. If for some reason one is not able to do prāṇāyāma in the morning it can also be done 5 hours after mid-day meals. If persons suffering from incurable diseases practise prāṇāyāma both in the morning and evening, they will soon benefit more.

Special precautions

- Those who are suffering from high B.P. and heart disease, should not practise bhastrikā at vigorous speed.
- We should not inflate our stomach while filling the breath inside during this prāṇāyāma. If you fill in the breath up to diaphragm

it will inflate the chest up to ribs, not the stomach. The name of diaphragmatic deep breathing only is bhastrikā.

- Practise it at a slow pace in summer season.
- Those whose both nostrils are not properly open due to excess of cough or sinus problems, etc, should first close the right nostril and do recaka and pūraka with left nostril. Then they should close the left nostril and do recaka and pūraka with the right nostril at slow, medium or vigorous speed as per their capacity. Then in the end, they should do bhastrikā prāṇāyāma using both iḍa end piṅgalā energy channels. One must practise this prāṇāyāma for 5 minutes daily. Keep your eyes closed while doing this prāṇāyāma and meditate on 'OM' in your mind with each inhalation and exhalation.

Benefits

- All kapha diseases like colds, catarrh, allergy, tuberculosis, asthma, chronic catarrh, sinusitis, etc, are cured. Lungs become strong and by getting purified air heart and mind also become healthy.
- All the throat diseases like thyroid and tonsilitis are cured.
- The three doṣas become balanced. Blood is purified and toxins and foreign matter are expelled from the body.
- Prāṇa and mind get stabilized. This is helpful in prāṇa- elevation and awakening of serpent power (kuṇḍalinī jāgaraṇa)

Second Procedure : Kapālabhāti Prāṇāyāma

Kapāla means 'brain, forehead', and bhati means 'glow, radiance, lustre, luminosity, etc.' The prāṇayāma which gives glow, radiance, lustre to the brain or forehead is called kapālabhāti. The procedure of this prāṇāyāma is a bit different from bhastrikā. In recaka and pūraka in the bhastrikā prāṇāyāma, equal pressure is exerted on inhalation and exhalation, while in kapālabhāti the whole attention is on recaka, i.e. exhaling vigorously. No effort is made to breathe in, the air that is breathed in naturally is allowed to be inhaled; the whole emphasis is on throwing the air outside. While doing this there is naturally contraction and expansion of abdomen and special force is exerted on mulādhāra (pelvic plexus), svādhiṣṭhāna (hypogastric plexus) and maṇipūra cakra (solar plexus).

The noble resolution (śiva saṅkalpa) during kāpalabhāti

While doing kapālabhāti prāṇāyāma one should resolve in mind that with the air exhaled by him all the diseases and disorders of the body are being thrown out, being eradicated. The recaka (exhalation) procedure should be performed with the feeling that he is expelling all the physical diseases and disorders as well as the mental flaws and distortions like lust, anger, greed, delusion, envy, attachment, aversion, etc. With this resolution of eradication of diseases and disorders while exhaling, one gets a lot of benefit.

Duration of Kapālabhāti prāṇāyāma

The breath should be exhaled in a rhythmic flow once in a second and should be held up effortlessly. If done non-stop kapālabhāti prāṇāyāma is done 60 times in one minute or 300 times in 5 minutes. Very sick and weak persons get tired in 2-3 minutes in the beginning, but in 10-15 days every person becomes capable of doing kapālabhāti non- stop for 5 minutes. Kapālabhāti must be done for 5 minutes in one sitting. One cannot get full benefit if it is done for a lesser time. With the increase in capacity after a long practice as well as with the maturity of experience one can do kapālabhāti prāṇāyāma up to 15 minutes. A healthy and even slightly sick person should do kapālabhāti for 15 minutes. In three rounds in 15 minutes kapālabhāti is done 900 times.

Persons suffering from incurable diseases like cancer, AIDS, hepatitis, leucoderma, vitiligo, psoriasis, excessive obesity, infertility, cysts/ nodules in uterus, ovary, breast or any where in the body, MS and SLE should do kapālabhāti for half an hour. It would be better if such incurable patients do kapālabhāti for half an hour both in the morning and evening. For healthy and slightly sick persons once a day is sufficient.

Benefits

- It increases glow, radiance, lustre and beauty of the face and brain.
- All kapha disorders like asthma, respiratory diseases, allergy, sinusitis etc are cured.
- All the diseases of heart, lungs and brain are cured.
- Obesity, diabetes, flatulence, constipation, acidity and kidney

and prostate diseases are definitely cured.

- With the regular practice of this prāṇāyāma for about 5 minutes daily, an obstinate disease like constipation is cured. Diabetes can be regulated without any medicine and the weight due to abdominal fat can be reduced by 4-6 kgs in one month. Blockages in the arteries of heart are removed.
- The mind remains stabilized, serene and cheerful. Negative thinking disappears and one gets rid of depression.
- The cakras are cleansed and a divine energy starts circulating in all the cakras, right from mulādhāra cakra (pelvic plexus) to sahasrāra cakra (cerebral gland).
- This prāṇāyāma especially improve the health of stomach, pancreas, liver, spleen, intestines, prostate and kidneys. Even if one does not get much benefit by doing many āsanas for stomach disorders, he can be benefited more than all the āsanas by doing only this prāṇāyāma. This is the best prāṇāyāma for giving strength to weak intestines.

Third procedure : Bāhya Prāṇāyāma (with three bandhas) :

Method:

- Sit properly in siddhāsana or padmāsana and throw the breath out, as much as you can, in one go.
- After throwing the breath out, apply mūlabandha, uddīyāna bandha and jālandhara bandha, and hold the breath out as much as you can.
- When you feel like breathing in, take the breath while relaxing the bandhas slowly.
- After taking in the breath, throw it out again as before, without holding it up.

The noble resolution (śiva saṅkalpa) during bāhya prāṇāyāma

Like kapālabhāti, in this prāṇāyāma also all the disorders and doṣas are being expelled while breathing out, this is what we should say to ourselves. We should know it for certain that the stronger is our power of thinking, the sooner will disappear all our afflictions. If our mind is inspired by a noble resolution, all our mental and physical diseases will be eradicated and we will be benefited all over.

Duration of bāhya prāṇāyāma

Filling in the breath effortlessly in 3-5 seconds, throwing it out effortlessly in 3-5 seconds, holding it out for 10-15 seconds, and again filling it in 3-5 seconds and doing bāhya prāṇāyāma by exhaling it, in this way bāhya prāṇāyāma is completed in about 20-25 seconds. It is better if two bāhya prāṇāyāmas are done non-stop one after the other. If in the beginning one has to take 1-2 normal breaths between two prāṇāyāmas, one may take them. Normally one can easily do bāhya prāṇāyāma 5 times in 2 minutes, and that is generally sufficient. Persons suffering from rectal prolapse, piles, fissure, fistula, vaginal prolapse, excessive urination, scanty urination and venereal diseases can practise it up to 11 times. Seekers desirous of awakening kuṇḍalinī and of being ūrdhvaretā (with upward movement of semen) may practise it maximum 21 times.

Benefits

It is a harmless prāṇāyāma. It dispels the unstability of mind. It improves the digestive power and is beneficial in stomach ailments. It makes the intellect sharp and subtle. It cleanses the body. By promoting the upward movement of semen, it removes the sexual disorders like nocturnal emissions, quick ejaculation, etc. In bāhya prāṇāyāma all the organs in the abdomen are strained a lot and slight pain is felt in the weak or diseased part of the abdomen in the beginning. Therefore, for giving some relaxation and therapy to the abdomen this prāṇāyāma should be done by applying the three bandhas.

Fourth procedure: Ujjāyī Prāṇāyāma

In this prāṇāyāma we contract the throat while doing the pūraka (inhaling) and when we breathe in by contracting the throat, we make a sound like snoring. We sit in a meditative pose and breathe in through both the nostrils. With some contraction of the throat we feet the friction of air in the throat. There should not be any friction of air in the nose. A sound is produced with the friction in the throat. In the beginning we should practise only pūraka- recaka (inhaling-exhaling) without applying kumbhaka (holding in). After the pūraka we should practise the kumbhaka gradually as long as the pūraka, and after practising for some days we should double the duration of kumbhaka. If the kumbhaka is to be done for more than 10 seconds, we should apply jālandhara- bandha and mūlabandha as well. In this prāṇāyāma we should always do the recaka (exhaling) with the left nostril and keep the right nostril closed.

Benefits

This prāṇāyāma is beneficial for those who suffer from colds, cough and catarrh throughout the year, for those who suffer from thyroid problems, snoring, sleep apnoea, heart disease, asthma, lungs diseases, for those who suffer from throat problems like tonsilitis, thyroid glands, etc, and for those who suffer from insomnia, mental stress, hypertension, dyspepsia, rheumatism, dropsy, tuberculosis, fever, spleen disorders, etc. It should be practised regularly to keep the throat fit, healthy and melodious. It is an excellent prāṇāyāma for awakening kuṇḍalinī, ajapā- japa, meditation, etc. It also rectifies the lispy (defective) speech of children.

Fifth procedure: Anuloma- Viloma Prāṇāyāma Method of closing the alternate nostrils

Raise your right hand and with its thumb close the right nostril (piṅgalā nāḍī) and while closing the left nostril use the ring finger and middle finger of the right hand. The palm of the hand should not be in front of the nose; it should instead be held away to the right side. (Vide Illustrations Nos. 2 and 3 at the outset).

Since iḍā nāḍī (left nostril) represents moon, lunar power, coolness and calmness, anuloma- viloma prāṇāyāma is started from the left nostril for cleansing the nāḍī (energy channel). Closing the right nostril with the right hand thumb, we should gently fill the breath inside through the left nostril. When the inhalation is complete, we should close the left nostril with the ring finger and middle finger of the right hand and exhale completely through the right nostril. The rate of inhalation-exhalation should gradually be increased from medium to vigorous. Inhale vigorously with full force and then exhale. Make the rate of inhaling and exhaling slow, medium or fast according to your capacity. If you do pūraka (inhaling) and recaka (exhaling) at a fast rate, there is a loud sound of breathing. After you have exhaled completely, keeping the left nostril closed, fill in complete breath through the right nostril and exhale it through the left nostril. Thus, one set is completed. You have to do this procedure non-stop, i.e. inhaling through the left nostril and exhaling through the right nostril, and then inhaling through the right nostril and exhaling through the left nostril. One starts feeling tired by repeating this series for one minute. When you feel tired, take some rest and begin the prāṇāyāma again when you feel better. Thus you can begin this prāṇāyāma by doing for 3 minutes and go up to 10 minutes. After practising regularly for a few days the capacity of a learner starts increasing, and in about a week he can do this prāṇāyāma non-stop up to five minutes.

With the constant practice of anuloma- viloma the energy lying in the mūlādhāra cakra (pelvic plexus) starts awakening. Vedas call it being ūrdhvaretas (one with an upward movement of semen), and in the language of modern yoga it is known as 'kuṇḍalinī jāgaraṇa' (awakening of serpent energy). While doing this prāṇāyāma one should chant and meditate upon 'OM' in his mind with each inhalation-exhalation. By doing so, the mind gets situated in the sublime state of dhyāna (meditation).

The noble resolution (śiva saṅkalpa) during anuloma viloma

While doing this prāṇāyāma, you should think in your mind that with the friction and churning of breath in iḍā and piṅgalā nāḍīs, suṣumṇā nāḍī is getting awakened. From the eight cakras right up to the sahasrāra cakra (cerebral gland) a celestial light is moving upward.

My whole body is aglow with a celestial light. As per illustration No. 16, one should meditate upon a celestial light, illumination and energy inside and outside the body, and realise 'oṁ khaṁ brahma'. One should think that God, the controller of universe, is suffusing him with divine energy and divine knowledge. Initiate yourself into the discipline of 'śaktipāta'. Guru (preceptor) is only a catalyst for attaining śakti (energy); he only connects you to divine vibrations. In fact, 'śaktipāta' (instilling of energy) is done by OM, the Supreme Lord, the limitless ocean of energy. Thus, by practising this anuloma-viloma prāṇāyāma, by getting suffused with divine vibrations, one will be blessed with a lot of physical, mental and spiritual benefit. A light will stir up automatically from mulādhāra cakra (pelvic plexus), kuṇḍalinī will awaken, you will become 'ūrdhvareta' (one with upward movement of semen) and will find yourself automatically suffused with divine energy.

Duration of anuloma- viloma prāṇāyāma

Filling in the breath with a rhythmic flow for about 2½ seconds through the left nostril, and without holding it up, throwing the breath out gently through the right nostril in about 2½ seconds, and immediately after throwing it out through the right nostril, filling in the breath effortlessly through the right nostril in 2½ seconds, and without holding it up, throwing it out in a rhythmic flow through the left nostril in about 2½ seconds. this procedure should be done non-stop for about 5 minutes. although it may be a bit tiresome in the beginning. Don't use too much of force and don't raise the elbow too high while doing anuloma-viloma – this will enable you gradually in 5-7 days to practise anuloma-viloma for 5 minutes at a stretch.

One set of anuloma-viloma prāṇāyāma will be performed in 10 seconds, i.e., 6 times in one minute. In a sitting of 5 minutes anuloma-viloma is performed about 30 times, and if a healthy person or a person suffering from light common ailments does it for the prescribed duration of 15 minutes, it will be performed about 90 times. Persons suffering from incurable diseases like cancer, leucoderma / vitiligo, psoriasis, muscular dystrophy, SLE, infertility, HIV, AIDS, kidney diseases, etc. should practise anuloma-viloma prāṇāyāma up to 30 minutes. When the practice gets perfected anulom-viloma prāṇāyāma can be done for 15 minutes or even half an hour at a stretch.

Benefits

- This prāṇāyāma cleanses seventy-two crore, seventy-two lakh, ten thousand, two hundred ten nāḍīs (energy channels). With the cleansing of all the nāḍīs the body becomes completely healthy, radiant and strong.
- All the vāta diseases like arthritis, rheumatism, gout, Parkinson's Disease, nervous debility, etc., all pitta diseases like urinary diseases, tissue diseases, spermatorrhea, emissions, hyperacidity, heart burn, skin rashes etc., all kapha diseases like colds, catarrh, chronic rhinitis, sinusitis, asthma, cough, tonsils, etc., are cured. All the three doṣas are pacified.
- Blockages in the arteries of heart are removed. With the regular practice of this prāṇāyāma, almost 30-40% blockages are removed in 3-4 months. We have tried it on a number of patients.
- All disorders of cholesterol, triglycerides, HDL, LDL, etc are removed.
- Negative thinking is transformed into increasingly positive

thinking. One starts attaining bliss, zest and fearlessness.

- In short, this prāṇāyāma purifies the body, the mind, the thoughts and the dispositions. All the diseases of the body are cured, and the mind is cleansed and gets absorbed in the meditation of 'oṁkāra'.

By doing this prāṇāyāma 250-500 times, the serpent power (kuṇḍalinī śakti) which lies with head downward in the pelvic plexus (mūlādhāra cakra) holds its head upward, and the process of kuṇḍalinī- awakening sets in.

N.B.

To know more about it and the precautions related to it, please refer to the chapter 'Ways of kundalini- awakening and precautions'.

Sixth Procedure: Bhrāmarī Prāṇāyāma

Inhale completely, press lightly at the root of the nose near the eyes with the middle fingers of both hands, keep the mind centred on the medullary plexus (ājñā- cakra). Close both the ears completely with thumbs. (Vide Illustration No.4 at the outset). Now, humming like a bee and resonating 'OM', breathe out. Repeat this procedure.

The noble resolution (śiva saṅkalpa) during bhrāmarī prāṇāyāma

This prāṇāyāma should be done by identifying your consciousness with divine consciousness and God's existence. One should have in one's mind this divine resolution or thought that God's compassion, peace and bliss is raining on him. God is enriching him with pure intellect (ṛtambharā prajñā) by dispelling all his ignorance with His divine light illumining his ājñā cakra (medullary plexus). Thus by doing this prāṇāyāma with pure intentions one feels a nebula of light in his ājña - cakra and starts going into meditation automatically.

Duration of bhrāmarī prāṇāyāma

Inhaling for 3-5 seconds, and closing the ears, eyes, etc, as per the procedure, breathing it out in 15-20 seconds, makes one set of bhrāmarī prāṇāyāma. After completing one set, one should again breathe in for 3-5 seconds with a rhythmic flow, and humming like a bee breathe it out in 15-20 seconds according to procedure. Thus, everybody should do bhrāmarī prāṇāyāma at least 5-7 times non-stop, which will take about 3 minutes. Those who are suffering from cancer, depression, Parkinson's Disease, migraine, heart disease and some other incurable disease or who are desirous of fathoming the depths of yoga can do bhrāmarī prāṇāyāma 11-21 times.

Benefits

It dispels the instability/ fickleness of mind and is beneficial in mental tension, agitation, high B.P, heart disease, etc. It is very useful for meditation.

Seventh procedure : Udgītha Prāṇāyāma

Inhale for 3-5 seconds in a rhythmic flow, and breathe it out in about 15-20 seconds while chanting the sacred word 'OM' methodically. After one chanting is complete one should again breathe deep inside for 3-5 seconds in a rhythmic flow and breathe it out in 15-20 seconds chanting 'OM'. Thus, everybody must do udgītha prāṇāyāma about 7 times in about 3 minutes. Those who are suffering from incurable diseases and the learners (sādhakas) desirous of fathoming the depths of meditation can do udgītha prāṇāyāma for 5-10 minutes or even longer. Both bhrāmarī and udgītha are gentle and effortless prāṇāyāmas. Therefore, if a sādhaka practises them for longer duration there is no possibility of any sort of harm.

Eighth Procedure : Praṇava Prāṇāyāma

After doing all the aforesaid prāṇāyāmas, concentrate your mind on inhalation and exhalation, and meditate upon udgītha (OM) with your prāṇa. God has made poles in the shape of 'Oṁkāra'. This piṇḍa (body) and this brahmāṇḍa (universe) – both are in the form of 'Oṁkāra'. 'Oṁkāra' is not a particular person or figure; it is a divine power which is controlling and regulating the whole universe. Turn yourself into a spectator (=Soul) and while inhaling deeply and exhaling subtly your respiration rate should be so subtle that you do not feel like hearing the sound of your breath, and even if one puts a cotton swab before your nose it should not shake or quiver. Gradually increase the practice and try to breathe in and breathe out once in one minute. Thus, try to look at the breath inside. In the beginning the friction of breath will be felt on the tip of nose. Gradually you shall be able to feel the touch of breath deep inside you. Thus, by chanting 'Oṁkāra' with every breath as a spectator (=Soul), one starts going into meditation automatically. Your mind will become highly one-pointed, absorbed in and identified with 'Oṁkāra'. Along with 'praṇava' the great Gāyatrī mantra from the Vedas should be chanted and recited, imbibing its meaning. Thus, through meditation a seeker can become identified with Brahman, the very essence of Existence, Consciousness and Bliss, and can attain the unique divine ecstasy of samādhi. Even while going to bed one should meditate into sleep, By doing this his sleep will be blessed with yoga; he will get rid of nightmares and will have a quick and sound sleep.

Duration of praṇava prāṇāyāma

When as a spectator (=Soul) we concentrate our mind on the rhythmic flow of breaths, the prāṇa gets subtle automatically, and we inhale once in 10-20 seconds and exhale in 10-20 seconds. Through long practice a yogi takes one breath in one minute. After bhastrikā, kapālabhāti, bāhya prāṇāyāma, anuloma-viloma, bhrāmarī and udgītha, this praṇava prāṇāyāma is done, which is another form of vipaśyanā or prekṣā dhyāna. It is completely meditation-based. Everybody must do this meditation-based prāṇāyāma. Yogis practising samādhi do this penance of breathing accompanied with meditation of praṇava for hours together, according to the availability of time. There is no sound of breathing in this procedure, i.e., this soundless penance takes a seeker into the deep silence within, where his senses merge in the mind, the mind in the prāṇa and the prāna in the Soul, and through Soul a seeker realizes the universal Soul, supreme Soul and Brahman. It is the path which has prāṇāyāma as its starting point from where it gradually and spontaneously leads from the constant practice of prāṇāyāma to pratyāhāra (withdrawal), from the constant practice of pratyāhāra to dhāraṇā (concentration), from the firm and constant practice of dhāraṇā to dhyāna (meditation), and from the constant practice of dhyāna to samādhi (absorption). With this prāṇa-sādhanā (prānāyāma), there is a union of dhāraṇa, dhyāna and samādhi, and saṁyama is attained (**trayamekatra saṁyamaḥ**). From saṁyama a sādhaka attains prajñāloka, which gives him self-healing, which ultimately blesses him with the experience of self-realization. He is encompassed by a dazzling aura which works as an impenetrable armour to protect the sādhaka (seeker) from all diseases, disorders and polluting influences.

OTHER PRAṆĀYĀMAS USEFUL FOR TREATING THE DISEASES

1. Sūryabhedī or Sūryāṅga Prāṇāyāma

Sit in a meditative pose, do the pūraka (inhaling) through the right nostril, then do the kumbhaka (holding in) by applying jālandhara bandha and mūlabandha, and in the end do the recaka (exhaling) through the left nostril. The duration of antaḥkumbhaka (holding in) should gradually be increased. This prāṇāyāma should be done 3, 5 or 7 times, and up to 10 after practising for some time. While doing kumbhaka one should meditate on the radiance of sun. In summer season, this prāṇāyāma should be done for a short duration.

Benefits

It increases heat and pitta (bile) in the body. It is beneficial in vāta- and kapha- origin diseases, blood and skin disorders, worms in stomach, leprosy, gonorrhoea, contagious diseases, dyspepsia, indigestion, female diseases, etc. It helps awaken kuṇḍalinī and delays the onset of old age. This prāṇāyāma should be done for a short duration after anuloma-viloma. By doing sūryabhedī prāṇāyāma without kumbhaka, heart rate and work efficiency of the body improve and weight is reduced, for which it is essential to do 27 rounds twice a day.

2. Candrabhedi or Candrāṅga Prāṇāyāma

In this prāṇāyāma, do the pūraka (inhaling) through the left nostril, and then do the antaḥ-kumbhaka (holding in, retaining the breath). It is better to do it with jālandhara-bandha and mūlabandha. Then do the recaka (exhaling) through the right nostril. In this prāṇāyāma the pūraka is always done through candrasvara (left nostril) and the recaka through sūryasvara (right nostril). Sūryabhedī is just opposite. While doing the kumbhaka, meditate on the light of full moon. It should be practised for a short duration in winter season.

Benefit

With the feeling of coolness in the body, fatigue and heat are relieved. It calms the agitations of mind. It is useful in the burning felt due to pitta.

3. Karṇarogāntaka Prāṇāyāma

In this prāṇāyāma, after doing the pūraka (inhaling) through both nostrils, we close the mouth and both nostrils and push the inhaled air out, It is like making an effort to breathe out through the ears. When the air presses toward the ears, there is automatically a sort of sound in the ears. Give 4-5 upward pushes to the breath and then do the recaka (exhaling) through both nostrils. It is sufficient to do it 2-3 times.

Benefits

It is beneficial for ear diseases and especially cures deafness.

4. Śītalī Prāṇāyāma

Sit in a meditative pose with your hands resting on the knees. Corrugating (shaping into a groove) your tongue and keeping your mouth open, do the pūraka (inhaling) through the mouth. Drawing the breath inside slowly through the groove in the tongue fill the lungs completely. Retain it for a few moments and then closing the mouth, do the recaka (exhaling) through both nostrils. Afterwards, corrugating the tongue, do the pūraka through the mouth and the recaka through the nose. Thus, as required for the disease, it can be done 5-10 times. Practise it less in the winter.

Special Instructions

You can also apply jālandhara-bandha while doing the kumbhaka (retaining). Persons with kapha constitution and those with tonsil disorders should not do śītalī and sītkārī prāṇāyāmas.

Benefits

- It is beneficial for the diseases of tongue, mouth and throat. Abdominal tumors, spleen disorders, fever, dyspepsia, etc are cured.
- By perfecting it one conquers hunger-thirst, this is what the yoga scriptures say.
- It lowers the high B.P., is useful in the diseases of pitta origin, and also purifies the blood.

5. Sītkārī Prāṇāyāma

Sit in a meditative pose, stick your tongue to the ceiling of your palate clench the upper and lower teeth and keep the lips open. Now gradually making the 'sī, sī' sound, breathe in through the mouth and fill the lungs completely. Apply jālandhara-bandha and stay as long as you can conveniently. Then close the mouth and gently do the rceaka through the nose. Repeat this likewise. It can be practised according to one's disease or need.

Special Instructions

- This prāṇāyāma can be practised without kumbhaka and jālandhara bandha.
- During the pūraka, the teeth and tongue should remain unmoved at their prescribed position.

Benefits

- Its modes, properties and benefits are like śītalī prāṇāyāma.
- Besides curing dental diseases and pyorrhea, etc., it cures the diseases of throat, mouth, nose and tongue.
- Sleeping duration is reduced and the body remains cool.
- It is beneficial in high B.P., if done 10-20 times.

6. Mūrcchā Prāṇāyāma

In this prāṇāyāma, while doing the pūraka (inhaling) with both nostrils we close our eyes and throw our head backward so that the gaze is fixed at the sky. Then we apply antaḥ- kumbhaka, and in the end we bring our head into normal position and gently do the recaka (exhaling). Again, without taking rest we do the pūraka, sky- gazing, kumbhaka–all of them together, and resume the earlier position. It is sufficient to do it 5 times daily.

Benefits

It is beneficial for headache, migraine, Parkinson's Disease, nervous debility, etc. It is useful for improving the eyesight and memory. It helps awaken kuṇḍalinī and is helpful in meditation by turning the mind inward.

7. Plāvinī Prāṇāyāma

It is a sort of vāyu- dhauti (air wash). As you drink water with your mouth, similarly keep on sucking air till the whole abdomen is filled with it. Then you have to burp (belch) so that the whole sucked in air is thrown out of the abdomen. By sucking in air, the polluted air is expelled from the mouth.

Benefits

It helps cure all stomach ailments and hysteria. It destroys the worms and improves the appetite/ digestive system. Polluted air is expelled.

8. Kevalī Prāṇāyāma

In this prāṇāyāma, only pūraka-recaka (inhaling-exhaling) is done, not the kumbhaka (retaining). The word 'OM' is mentally resonated during pūraka (inhaling) as well as recaka (exhaling). Thus with each inhalation and exhalation the mental 'ajapā- japa' of 'OM' in the form of 'udgītha' goes on incessantly.

Benefit

Concentration is achieved soon and 'ajapā- japa' is perfected.

9. Nāḍī- śodhana Prāṇāyāma

To start with, in nāḍī- śodhana prāṇāyāma, like anuloma-viloma prāṇāyāma, we should close the right nostril and inhale gently through the left nostril. When the inhalation is completed we should hold the prāṇa inside according to our capacity and apply mūlabandha and jālandhara- bandha. We should breathe out very gently through the right nostril. When the exhalation is completed, we should inhale gently through the right nostril and do antaḥ-kumbhaka (holding in). Holding in the breath as per our capacity, we should gently breathe out throught our left nostril. Thus one round or one set of nāḍī-śodhana prāṇāyāma is completed. If this procedure is done with mental concentration without touching the nostrils with your hand, it is more beneficial, because in this way the concentration of your mind is centred on prāṇa and the mind attains absolute stability. There should not be any sound of breathing while inhaling and exhaling. This prāṇāyāma must be done at least 1-3 times, even more at will. The ratio of pūraka, antaḥkumbhaka and recaka in nāḍī-śodhana prāṇāyāma in the beginning should as much as possible be 1: 2: 2:, i.e., if we do the pūraka in 10 seconds, we should do the antaḥkumbhaka for 20 seconds, and then gently do the recaka (exhaling) in 20 seconds. Afterwards take this ratio to 1: 4: 2. When you have reached this level, you can also add bāhya- kumbhaka (holding the breath out) to it, i.e., now the ratio of pūraka, antaḥkumbhaka, recaka and bāhyakumbhaka will be 1: 4: 2: 2.

This prāṇāyāma should be done at a very slow speed. The longer and subtler the speed of prāṇa (breath), by doing this prāṇāyāma effortlessly without being particular about the number of times you do it, the more beneficial will it be for you. Inhaling, exhaling and retaining as per your capacity is the real ratio factor in this prāṇāyāma. If you do it this way, you don't need any rest in between. While doing pūraka, kumbhaka and recaka, you should do in your mind japa (recitation) and meditation of 'OM' or Gāyatrī Mantra.

Benefits

All the benefits are like those of anuloma-viloma prāṇāyāma. It is especially beneficial in muscular dystrophy, MS, SLE, polio, neuropathy and auto- immune disease. This prāṇāyāma helps control the senses, mind and prāṇa.

ENERGY CENTRES OR CAKRAS LOCATED IN THE BODY

The cakras located in human body are the centres of various types of marvellous powers. All these cakras are linked together starting from the root to the top of the spinal cord. In normal state they lie undeveloped with face downward, like an un blown lotus. When they blow up with face upward, on getting the right stimulus through observance of celibacy, prāṇāyāma and yogic procedures like meditation etc., their supernatural powers are developed. The concrete pictures of cakras are merely symbolical in conveying the idea of their subtle nature. Similarly the English terminology like pelvic plexus, etc does not convey their actual location; it gives a mere indication.

A Brief Description of Cakras

The holy Atharvaveda says about cakras :

aṣṭācakrā navadvārā devānāṁ pūrayodhyā /
tasyāṁ hiraṇyayaḥ kośaḥ svargo jyotiṣāvṛtaḥ //
(ATHARVAVEDA: 10.2.31)

In this body (Ayodhya), the gods' city, there are eight turnpikes (cakras) and nine gates (two eyes, two nostrils, two ears, mouth, anus, urinary organ). In this city there is a glittering golden treasure- chest which is overflowing with endless, immense, limitless happiness, peace, bliss and celestial luminosity. Only a seeker practising yoga can get this celestial treasure- chest. Now we give a brief description of cakras.

1. Mūlādhāra Cakra (Pelvic / Root Plexus vis- a- vis Reproductory System)

This cakra is located two digits above the base of anus and two digits below the base of urinary organ. Suṣumṇā nāḍī (Sarasvatī) runs through its centre and the Iḍa nāḍi (Gaṅgā) through its left corner. Therefore, it is called 'Mukta Triveṇī'. By virtue of its being the base of root energy, i.e. kuṇḍalinī śakti, it is called 'mūlādhāra cakra'. By meditating on this cakra one develops good health and qualities like efficiency and work-skill. With the awakening of this cakra a man becomes ūrdhvaretā (one with upward movement of semen), radiant and energetic, and all the diseases of his body are eradicated.

Illustration No. 5 (at the outset) shows that this first cakra, mūlādhāra, is being illuminated by mānasa raśmis (mental rays) kindled by savitā (radiance of intellect). In this spot a soft light as that of a fountain or a torch is emitting from that fibre which runs in front of the svādhiṣṭhāna cakra (hypogastric plexus) up to the mūlādhāra. Tenebrous darkness is deeply rooted here. This darkness is dispelled by cultivation of prāṇa and dhāraṇā-dhyāna (concentration-meditation), and mūlādhara is illuminated. This illumination lays bare all the grossness and subtlety held in the mūlādhāra. This is also called 'kuṇḍalinī jāgaraṇa' (awakening of serpent power). Illustration No. 5 shows (1) top of suṣumṇā, (2) lower part of the abdomen linked with this cakra, (3) pink coloured small intestines, (4) yellow coloured large intestines, (5) pelvis in the lower part of large intestines (rectum and anus), (6) coccyx (lower end of the vertebral column), (7) lower passage of suṣumṇā, (8) suṣumṇā (main fibre), the lower end of suṣumṇā, (9) all the mūlādhāra region being illuminated.

2. Svādhiṣṭhāna Cakra (Hypogastric plexus vis- a- vis Excretory system)

This cakra is located near the hypogastrium two digits above the mūlādhāra cakra. According to Tantra literature, the fruit of meditating on this cakra is the capability of creation, preservation and decimation and invocation of Sarasvatī on one's tongue.

It is clearly shown in Illustration No. 6 (at the outset) that the svādhiṣṭhāna cakra is located in the hypogastrium. This cakra contains the urinary system which comprises (1) right-left kidneys, (2) urinary bladder, (3) the posterior part of urinary organ, (4) urine-carrying ducts branching off the kidneys, in which the green leaves are (5) semen- cells, with the semen- carrying ducts on right and left, the semen- manufacturing mechanism, (6) testes, (7) prostate gland, semen-carrying and urine- carrying ducts and the excretory passage for semen and urine, (8) penis. With the realization of this cakra one gets to know about 'urinary system' and ' seminal system' and their mutual relation.

3. Maṇipūra Cakra (Epigastric Plexus or Solar Plexus vis- a-vis Digestive System)

It is located at the root of navel. This cakra provides energy to the whole digestive system (liver, intestines, etc.) and pancreas, etc. In a Yogadarśana Sūtra: **nābhicakre kāyavyūhajñānam** (3.22), the fruit of meditating on the navel centre has been stated to be the knowledge of anatomy, i.e., the knowledge of the location of various organs in the body. With the awakening of this cakra, diabetes, constipation, indigestion, flatulence–all disorders of metabolism are cured.

Illustration No. 7 (at the outset) shows the location of maṇipūra cakra. It is located behind the navel and comprises (1) stomach, (2) liver, (3) spleen, (4) pancreas, and (5) small bowel.

4. Hṛdaya Cakra or Nimna Manaścakra (Lower Mind Plexus vis- a- vis Skeleton System)

This cakra is located near the heart. The Tantra literature speaks of oratorical skills, poetic talent and conquest over senses among its benefits. Śivasāratantra says that the anāhata dhvani (anhad nād, unstruck sound) originating from this spot is udgītha (Oṁkāra) which is always beneficent to all. This cakra is appropriate for concentration (dhāraṇā) and meditation (dhyāna) by women and sentimental devotees. One who meditates on this cakra can never suffer from heart disease. (Vide illustration No.8 at the outset).

5. AnāhataCakra(CardiacPlexusvis-a-visCirculatorySystem)

This cakra is located between the two breasts. With the awakening and becoming healthy of mūlādhāra, svādhiṣṭhāna and maṇipūra cakras, this cakra is automatically awakened. As a result of its awakening, bones and muscles start getting healthy and strong. Divine virtues like love, compassion, service and sympathy are developed by meditaling on this cakra. Maharṣi Vyāsa also exhorts about meditating on the hṛdaya cakra. It is not the gross but the emotional aspect of heart, which is related to the mind or psyche of a person. (Vide Illustration No.9)

In Illustration No.9 (at the outset), anāhata cakra has been magnified. The central spheres of the heart-lotus (hṛdaya puṇḍarīka) have been clearly shown here.

6. Viśuddhi Cakra (Carotid Plexus vis- a- vis Respiratory System)

Its location is in the throat. By meditating on this cakra and on its awakening one becomes a poet, savant, healthy person, free of sorrows and long- living. With the awakening of this cakra one does not suffer from thyroid and lung diseases. Illustration No. 10 (at the outset) describes the viśuddhi cakra in which the numbers in 'A' section show the trachea (1) and the relation between the interiors of both lungs (4).

7. Ājñā Cakra (Medullary Plexus vis- a- vis Nervous system)

This cakra is located in the middle spot between the two eyebrows. With prāṇāyāmas like kapālabhāti, anuloma-viloma, nāḍīśodhana, etc., the mind and prāṇa become calm and stable which makes the autonomic and voluntary nervous system tranquil, healthy and balanced. The whole nāḍī system is connected with the ājñā cakra. With the awakening of ājña cakra the nādī system becomes completely healthy and strong. Iḍā, piṇgalā and suṣumṇā flowing upward as separate streams out of the mūlādhāra cakra (pelvic plexus) make a confluence on this spot (i.e., ājña cakra). Therefore, this spot is also called Triveṇī. In Illustration No. 10 in the beginning of this book, the two ball- like things in section B represent the spot of ājñā cakra; the light with the upward flame is that of suṣumṇā.

iḍā bhāgīrathī gaṅgā piṅgalā yamunā nadī /
tayormadhyagatā nāḍī suṣumṇākhyā sarasvatī //
triveṇī- saṅgamo yatra tīrtharājaḥ sa ucyate /
tatra snānaṁ prakurvīta sarvapāpaiḥ pramucyate //
(JÑĀNASAṄKALINĪTANTRA)

Iḍā is called Gaṅgā, piṅgalā Yamunā, and the suṣumṇā nāḍī running between the two is called Sarasvatī. The spot of confluence of this Triveṇī is called Tīrtharāja. The seeker who immerses himself in it is purged of all his sins. This Triveṇī-confluence is not outside; it is inside us. 'A person is purged of his sins by immersing himself in the worldly (outside) Triveṇī– it is an illusion, a fallacy. If that be possible, then anybody murdering a brahmin, preceptor or brother, etc. should be purged of his sins by taking a dip in Triveṇi Saṅgama, but it does not happen. Sin (pāpa) means 'crime, misdeed' which causes harm to others. Therefore, one has to bear the fruit (penalty) of sin. After committing a sin, even if you do a meritorious deed in the form of an atonement, you have to bear different types of returns/ rewards–unhappiness as the reward for sins and happiness as the reward for meritorious deeds. Therefore, the scriptures say:

avaśyameva bhoktavyaṁ kṛtaṁ karma śubhāśubham. But if a person sincerely bathes in Gaṇgā or Triveṇī, and after the bath makes this resolution that he is not going to commit any sinful deed throughout his life, he can be saved from sin in the future by dint of his sacred vow and resolution. But one cannot escape the sin committed until now. This is what we have to say about external Triveṇī, but if a person fixes his mind in the Triveṇī- saṇgama located in the ajñā cakra by practising prāṇāyāma and meditation and immerses himself in God's devotion and the Gaṇgā of knowledge, there is hardly any possibility of his committing a sin. Therefore, if we really want to get rid of sins, we should daily fix our mind in the ajñā cakra and practise yoga, chanting and reciting oṁkāra.

8. Sahasrāra Cakra (Endocrine System)

This cakra located in the cerebrum above the fontanelle (brahmarandhra) is the centre of all divine powers. By fixing and restraining the prāṇa (life–breath) and mind on this cakra, the mental modifications, viz. pramāṇa (correct knowledge), viparyaya (mistaken knowledge), vikalpa (illusory/ imaginary knowledge), nidrā (dreamless sleep) and smṛti (remembering), are restrained, and asamprajñāta (ultra-cognitive) samādhi is attained. All the endocrine glands, including the pituitary and the pineal, are connected with the sahasrāra cakra. With the awakening of the sahasrāra cakra the whole endocrine system gets balanced.

Yoga scholars maintain that the thumb- size hṛdaya- puruṣa alluded to in the Upaniṣads is nothing else but this brahmarandhra, above which the sahasrāra cakra is located. This is where the Mind resides, and which is being illuminated by the light of knowledge of the Soul.

Where does the Soul (jīvātmā) reside in the body? It is a complicated question whether the light of knowledge of the Soul illumines the Mind (citta). The Mind (citta) is, in a way, subtle body. Only on getting coupled with this subtle body the Soul is called jīvātmā (embodied soul). The causal body permeates the subtle body. Thus jīvātmā permeates the whole body. Even then, due to its different functions, it is said to reside in several places.

Normally in the sleeping state (suṣupti- avasthā) the jīvātma resides in heart- region (hṛdaya deśa) because heart is the main centre of the body. From here the nāḍīs branch off to the whole body. The internal workings of the body stop at this point. Therefore, in the sleeping state (suṣupti- avasthā) the jīvātmā can be said to be residing in the heart. Upaniṣads also say this:

yatraiṣa etat supto 'bhūd ya eṣa vijñānamayaḥ
puruṣastadeṣāṁ prāṇānāṁ vijñānena vijñānamādāya
ya eṣo' ntarhṛdaya ākāśastasmiñchete (BṚHAD. 2.1.96)

"When this puruṣa (=Soul), who is full of supreme intellect (vijñāna), is in sound sleep, then by the vijñāna of senses, along with vijñāna, he rests in the space which is there in the heart."

In the dream state (svapnāvasthā) the jīva (embodied soul) resides in the throat, because the size of impressions of the objects seen, heard or enjoyed in the awakened state is one thousandth of the thickness of a hair. Therefore, in the dream state the subtle perception in the form of impressions of experienced objects is in the throat, because in the awakened state the jīvātmā perceives the external objects by external sense organs in which eyes hold a prominent place; therefore, in the awakened state the jīvātmā is said to be residing in the eyes.

ya eṣo 'kṣiṇi puruṣo dṛsyata eṣa ātmeti. (CHĀNDO. 1.2.6)

"This puruṣa that is seen in the eye is ātmā." In samprajñāta (cognitive samādhi) the jīvātmā can be said to reside in ājñā- cakra (because this is the repository of divine vision). This is also called divyanetra or 'Śivanetra'. In asamprajñāta (ultra-cognitive) samādhi, the jīvātmā is said to reside in brahmarandhra. When the Mind and the Prāṇa are stabilized on this, then asamprajñāta (ultra-cognitive) samādhi, i.e. the restraining of all vṛttis, is attained. In Illustration No 10 (at the outset), section B, (1) topmost end of suṣumṇā, (2) cerebellum, (3) the 'Sheath of Intellect' or 'subtle body,' a conglomerate of mind+intellect+ 10 sense organs, surrounded by 5 tanmātras (subtle elements), (4) brahmarandhra (sahasrāra), (5) part of cerebrum, where '3' (marked in red) is called the 'adhipati randhra'.

KUṆḌALINĪ-ŚAKTI (SERPENT POWER)

The divine power lying in the mūlādhāra cakra has been called kuṇḍalinī śakti (serpent power) in the latter-day Tantra literature, and brahmavarcas (radiance of brahman) in the Vedic literature. Normally prāṇaśakti (life force) flows through iḍā and piṅgalā nāḍis only. When one practises prāṇāyāma and yogic procedures like meditation, etc. with proper restraint, then the marvellous power lying dormant in suṣumṇā nāḍī starts developing. The power which was being consumed in sensual enjoyments is transformed by the practice of yoga and it starts moving upward. Philosophers like Plato and Pythagoras have given a similar hint in their writings that there lies a divine power near the navel which illumines the sovereignty of cerebrum, ie. the light of intellect, by which divine powers start developing in a person.

CAKRA-ŚODHANA (CLEANSING OF CAKRAS) OR KUṆḌALINĪ JĀGARAṆA (AWAKENING OF SERPENT POWER)

Whatever energy is in the cosmos (brahmāṇḍa), the same exists in this body-**yathā piṇḍe ṭathā brahmāṇde.** The main base/support of energy is the mūlādhāra cakra. With the awakening of this cakra the divine energy starts moving upward; this is the awakening of kuṇḍalinī. All the network of electric wires and bulbs, etc. is controlled by the main switch. When the main switch is pressed 'on', then the electricity flows into the whole network, and there is light everywhere. Similarly, with the awakening of the divine electrical energy lying dormant in the mūlādhāra carkra, there is an automatic awakening of other cakras.

When this kuṇdalinī energy ascends and upsurges, one attains samprajñāta (cognitive) samādhi when it reaches particular spots, and when it reaches the sahasrāra cakra, then due to all the vṛitis (movements of the mind) being restrained, one attains asamprajñāta (ultra-cognitive) samādhi. In this very state the divine light of knowledge hidden in the mind starts revealing itself, which makes a seeker attain ṛtambharā prajñā (pure intellect) and ṛealize the whole truth. At last, after attaining this ṛtambharā prajñā a seeker is blessed with the immense, eternal bliss of nirbīja samādhi. This is the climax of yoga. On attaining this state, with the eradication of all desires/ tendencies in the form of impressions, a sādhaka lives a liberated existence and enjoys the eternal bliss of liberation.

WAYS OF AWAKENING KUṆḌALINĪ

Under Siddhayoga the awakening of kuṇḍalinī is done by śaktipāta' (bestowing of energy). If one is able to get a highly accomplished ascetic guru, he can bestow that tremendous energy with his mental resolution, and that 'psychic divine energy' permeating the body clusters, and at the time of meditation it becomes a stream of light or activity and flows through the body. This radiance replete with self- consciousness starts functioning as a sentient principle. With the energy bestowed (śaktipāta) by a noble preceptor (sadguru) a seeker does not have to work very hard, his time is saved, and he gains success quickly in his penance (sādhanā). But it is of utmost importance that one gets such an accomplished guru who can bestow energy (śaktipāta). Therefore, at present the awakening of kuṇḍalinī through pranic energy has become quite significant. In yoga, the body is purified in the yoga- fire (yogāgni) by procedures like ṣaṭkarma, āsana, prāṇāyāma, mudrās, bandhas, etc. After the nāḍis have been cleansed through the disciplining of prāṇa, the sense organs are diverted inward through the practice of pratyāhāra (withdrawal). With the stabilization of mind through dhāraṇā (concentration) a seeker conquers the five elements–earth, water, fire, air and space. Penetrating the cakras and by awakening the kuṇḍalinī through dhyāna (meditation), the embodied soul (jīvātmā) realises Parama Śiva (Supreme Good). If one sits in a meditative pose with the spine erect, the 'prāṇa' starts flowing easily into the nāḍī- plexuses originating from the central spinal cord (suṣumṇā). With a bent spinal cord the nerve-plexuses become contracted and get clogged with unnecessary and obstructive phlegm, etc., and remain unclean due to lack of prāṇa- circulation in them. The disciplining of prāṇa by practising yoga impacts the prāṇamaya kośa (vital air sheath), by which all the parts of prāṇamaya kośa get stimulated and the rate of blood-circulation is accelerated, and then the organs expel through the passages of lungs, skin and eyes the waste products like phlegm, mucus, etc. deposited at various spots. As a result, there are various types of reactions in the body and one feels exhilarated.

In yoga terminology it is prāṇotthāna' (elevation of prāṇa) which is the first rung on the ladder of kuṇḍalinī rising. In this stage there are special sensory experiences originating from the dynamism of prāṇa. With continued practice, in the illumined latter-half of prāṇa-elevation, light is perceived at various spots in the body, and the latter- half of kuṇḍalinī awakening begins. Thus, by the disciplining (sādhanā) of prāṇa, prāṇamaya kośa is realized. All the kośas are linked up with prāṇa. Therefore, with the removal by prāṇāyāma of the impurities deposited in the cakras as well as the screen covering them, one realizes in course of time the cakras located in the body, the processes going on in the cakras, the powers hidden therein, the prāṇas and upa-prāṇas working here and there as well as the iṣus and adhipatis. When, by the continued practice of disciplining the prāṇa, sovereignty is established over the power inhabiting these cakras, then, with the capability of circulating at will the pranic energy from mulādhāra (root plexus) to sahasrāra (crown plexus), it becomes very easy to realize all the cakras and progressively all the kośas (sheaths). In Illustration No. 11 (at the outset), 'Sauṣumṇa Jyoti' shows that with the continued practice of prāṇāyāma the nāḍī-network is purified, and prāṇa and the whole course of suṣumṇā gets illuminated. The light of (2) the mind, impelled by (1) intellect, the main part of the 'subtle body' enclosed in the forehead, moves along the course of the apex for suṣumṇā, and illuminating the whole (4) 'nādi-pair', flows through the mūlādhāra cakra (root/pelvic plexus).

As the screen of tamas (darkness) decays with the continued practice of disciplining the prāṇa with complete dedication and perseverance, all the cakras, right from mūlādhāra to svādhiṣṭhāna (hypogastric plexus) to sahasrāra (crown plexus) at the top, start getting illuminated. Illustration No.12 (at the outset) shows the form of cakras prior to their being illuminated through perfection of prāṇāyāma. The one lowest at the bottom is showing the prior from of mūlādhāra cakra. The lowest at the bottom is the 'homakuṇḍa-shaped' mūlādhāra and the one above it is svādhiṣṭhāna cakra; the one above this is maṇipūra cakra located in the navel, the waves arising from this cakra surrounded by nāḍīs are those of anāhata śabda (unstruck sound); above this there are hṛdaya cakra and anāhata cakra glowing like the flame of a lamp in the chest; then there is the necklace-shaped viśuddhi cakra in the throat; and then on the top is sahasrāra cakra shining like a sun in the lotus.

A seeker sees at first only the prior form of these cakras. Later, when he is able to enter the internal body through meditation he attains all the extrasensory introspection and remote-sensing. Illustration No 13(at the outset)-[Form of Divya-dṛṣti]: the light of jīvātmā in the (1) psyche (citta) always keeps the psyche and the ego illuminated; impelling the vijñānamaya kośa (intellect sheath) located in the forehead through the pathways (4, 5) it inspires the mind (3), and by bestowing divinity on the inner eye, the mind (6) is making the inner eye (7) divine by its rays (5). The 'divya dṛṣti' (divine vision) (8) inspired by the power of determination of yogi reveals all the objects by the illumination of its rays (9) in the space (dyuloka) beyond the solar orb and up to the lowest subterranean world (pātāla) by penetrating into the womb of earth (1-10).

These energy-centres, i.e. cakras, are located in a subtle, seed-form in the luminous nāḍi which runs through the spinal cord and is called suṣumṇā. In Illustration No. 14 (at the outset), the first part shows the mysterious suṣumṇā, in which 1 represents the serpentine 'suṣumṇā' (in red) lying in the serpent-like spinal cord constituted of 33 vertebrae of different sizes. 'A' is the apex (head) of suṣumṇā which is linked to the cerebrum, and 'B' is its tail which joins the tail- bone or coccyx. The internal position of (2) suṣumṇā is being clarified by 'A': the pair of nāḍīs branching out from the middle of two vertebrae and spreading all over the body 'B': Viewing it after cutting off the outer cover of suṣumṇā clarifies the actual position of this nādī pair. 'C': It is a cross- section of suṣumṇā .'D': In the middle of each pair of vertebrae is a cushion (dise) of muscles. 'E': From 'D' to 'E', the nāḍī-pairs emerge in a similar way and are spreading all over the body. 'F': From top to bottom of the spine there are muscle- discs between all the vertebrae. In 3 and 5 there is a cross- section of suṣumṇā showing its internal side where there is a network of cognitive (jñānavahā) and dynamic (gativahā) nāḍīs thinner, subtle than the gossamer. This network works round the clock without resting for a second. In 5, suṣumṇā and along with it the two main nāḍīs 'iḍā' and 'piṅgalā' to its right and left go down from the top and join in front of the pelvic bone. The helix-like iḍā-piṅgalā look like a garland.

The main source of the circulation of vital energy in the whole body with the combination of 'cognition' (jñāna) and 'action' (kriyā) is only suṣumṇā.

The table at p. 121
shows cakras at a glance.

Thus it is clear that with the awakening of mūlādhāra cakra (root/ pelvic plexus) all other cakras (energy centres) start awakening automatically, and the divine energy starts ascending–this is what we call 'kuṇḍalinī jāgaraṇa.' Put in scientific terms, this kuṇḍalinī is that psychic cosmic force which permeates the whole body. A seeker should seek the guidance of some noble accomplished yoga- practitioner, and by disciplining his prāṇa he should cleanse, penetrate and awaken his cakras by the following main procedures:

- A seeker desirous of awakening his kuṇḍalinī should practise daily and methodically bhastrikā prāṇāyāma for 5 minutes, kapālabhāti for 30 minutes, bāhya prāṇāyāma 11-21 times and anuloma-viloma for 30 minutes with perseverance, rhythm, absorption, faith and sincerity. In the beginning, when one feels tired one can take rest in between. If one meditates on 'OM' with each breath while doing prāṇāyāma, the goal will be achieved sooner. After anuloma-viloma one must do bhrāmarī and udgītha for 5 minutes each, meditating upon the divine radiance. In the end one must go on inward journey by concentrating the mind along with prāṇa (life-breath). Thus, by meditating upon 'OṀKĀRA' along with prāṇa one can reach the highest firmament of yoga. The Japa (repeated recitation) of OṀKĀRA, through meditation creates the gradually widening circles of ripples in a sādhaka. These tickling or thrilling ripples cause electric vibrations (called taḍita due to their being developed on striking= tāḍanā of prāṇa) in svādhiṣṭhāna cakra through the medium of prāṇamaya kośa (nervous system) create a resonance (nāda) (inarticulate sound) in the navel region and a special sort of heat is felt in the stomach. The heat produced in the stomach is transformed into resolution (saṅkalpa). When the special sort of strike-vibration produced by Japa-dhyāna (recitation- meditation) enters the prāṇamaya kośa (nervous system) through the network of nerves in the form of electric waves, then a flow starts from our cerebrum and impacts the maṇipūra cakra in our navel through the network of nerves.

The purpose behind japa- dhyāna of 'OṀKĀRA' is that one should elevate prāṇa from low level to high level, and the intellect and the mind be lifted from the action-packed sphere of prāṇa to the level of vijñānamaya koṣa (sheath of intellect) and the 'mind- intellect' be brought to the level of ānandamaya kośa (sheath of bliss) and stabilized there. In other words, gradually dispense with the practice of body, prāṇa, etc., move over the prāṇamaya, manomaya and vijñānamaya kośas, mopping up the 'self- consciousness' permeating the body, stabilize it in 'ānandānugata' (blissful) and 'asmitānugata' (uniting self and intellect into one) samādhis (trances) or get yourself situated in it.

Besides praṇava, one can meditate upon Gāyatrī, the greatest of Vedic mantras, according to Illustration No 15 (at the outset). A sādhaka (seeker) should try to look inside his cerebellum (kapāla) lying in the cerebrum from the point of view of meditation, and should meditate that his cerebrum is filling up with a divine light at that particular moment, and is now completely filled up, an extremely white light as that of a moonbeam or an unflickering beam of light from a torch is entering into the yellowish- golden coloured sphere of his intellect (2). With the intellect (buddhi), the queen ruling over the vijñānamaya kośa, getting extremely pure and illumined, the 'mind', the sovereign lord of senses, and the "sense organs" subordinate to it are automatically getting cleansed, purified and sanctified. In such a state the ocean of bliss and the supremely serene and immense light in the brain and heart is in full tide day and night.

Besides Oṁkāra-recitation or Gāyatrī-recitation, a sādhaka may also meditate upon the divine light (divya āloka) according to Illustration No. 16 (at the outset). The supremely Radiant Thousand-eyed God (1) is bestowing 'brahmateja' on me, and 'brahmateja' is shining like the sun in my heart (2), and that God is in front of me in the form of a pure, graceful light, is manifested in my soul (3). I should always wish that this most divine light may forever illumine the path of my life, and may escort, accompany me throughout my life.

CAKRAS AT A GLANCE

NAME OF CHAKRAS	GROSS FORM	LOCATION	ELEMENT	SEED SYLLABLE	MAIN VĀYU	SECONDARY VĀYU	KOŚA (Sheath)	COSMIC SPHERE	DISEASES DUE TO LAXITY OR NON-AWAKENING OF CAKRAS
MULĀDHĀRA	pelvic plexus	approx. 1''inside between anus and genitals	earth	laṁ	apāna	kūrma	annamaya (food)	bhūḥ	infertility, tissue diseases, disorders of genitals
SVĀDHIṢ–ṬHĀNA	hypogas-tric plexus	1''-1.5'' above mūlādhāra (near hypogastrium)	water	vaṁ	vyāna	dhanañjaya	prāṇamaya (vital air)	bhuvaḥ	urinary disorders, kidney diseases, calculi, etc.
MAṆIPŪRA	epigastric sciar plexus	near navel	fire	raṁ	samāna	kṛkala	manomaya (mind)	svaḥ	all disorders of digestive system, diabetes, piles, etc.
HṚDAYACĀKRA OR MANAŚCAKRA	lower mind plexus	between the two breasts	diseases of bones and muscles						
ANĀHATA	cardiac plexus	heart	air	yaṁ	prāṇa	nāga	vijñāmaya (intellect)	mahaḥ	heart diseases, high B.P., etc.
VIŚUDDHI	carotid plexus	throat	space	haṁ	udāna	devadatta	ānandamaya (bliss)	janaḥ	asthma, lung disorders, etc.
ĀJÑĀCAKRA	medullary plexus	between eyebrows (a little behind cerebellum)	manas (mind)	om				tapaḥ	epilepsy, fainting, nervous system disorders, paralysis, etc.
SAHASRĀRA	cerebral gland	cerebellum (above fontanelle in the cerebrum)	mahattattva (pure potenti-ality)					satyaṁ	hormonal imbalance, metabolic syndrome, etc.

SOME GUIDELINES FOR MEDITATION

- While meditating, give meditation (dhyāna) the utmost importance. At the time of meditation, don't entertain any other thought howsoever noble or auspicious it may be. Giving charity, rendering service or good to others, studying, serving your guru and tending the cows, etc. are noble deeds, but while you are in meditation, don't think about them. At the time of meditation, the only aim of thought, contemplation, study or realization should be 'brahman'.
- At the time of meditation, turn your mind and senses inward, and before meditation you must think in your mind on these lines: "I am not matter, wealth, affluence, land, house, son, grandson, spouse, etc. All these manifest- unmanifest entities are not my true nature. I am independent of the bond of animate and inanimate external objects. This body also is not my true self. I am independent of the body, the sense organs and the enjoyments of senses in the form of sound, touch, sight, taste and smell, etc. I am independent of the mind and its distractions like lust, anger, greed, delusion and the five afflictions with abhiniveśa (fear of death) being one of them. I am the blissful, luminous, pure being. I am the child of immortality. I am related to that ocean of bliss, the Very Essence of Being, Consciousness and Bliss, the Almighty God, as a drop to the ocean; it evaporates from the sea and ascends to the sky, rains down to the earth and flowing in a river loses its identity into the ocean again; a drop cannot live without the ocean. I, a mere drop, also want to be an ocean by dissolving myself into the supreme Lord, the Ocean of Bliss. That Creator, Providence, Our Father, Supreme Lord has given us everything–life, breath, birth, age, body, intellect, physical comforts, house, family, parents, etc. That Lord is always showering bliss on me. His peace and supreme happiness is raining on me from all sides. That Blissful Mother and Supremely Protective Father does not separate me from Himself even for a moment. I am always in the Lord and the Lord is in me. This identification, this similarity and integrality with him will bestow supreme bliss upon us. God is raining this

bliss always and incessantly. Even then if we don't experience that bliss, it is our own fault.

- A sādhaka (seeker) should always have an attitude of discernment (viveka) and non-attachment (vairāgya). He should do all noble deeds as a service to God in a non-attached manner by situating himself as a seer, spectator (=soul). The performance of one's duty without any ego or any expectation of its reward is practical meditation.
- The thought of external happiness and the means of pleasure ultimately cause misery. As long as the mind seeks happiness in worldly things, it will be impossible to attain surrender to God, and the meditation and absorption (samādhi) leading to complete dedication to God (īśvarapraṇidhāna).
- Therefore, every seeker of liberation (mumukṣu) should devote at least one hour daily to recitation, meditation and worship. By doing this he can end all his miseries in this birth and realize the supreme Lord, our Great Father. It should always be remembered that the main aim of life is self-realization and attainment of God; all other actions and aims are secondary. If we don't start marching right now in our life on the path of God-realization, the Upaniṣad seers observe:

iha cedavedīdatha satyamasti
na cedihāvedīnmahatī vinaṣṭiḥ /
bhūteṣu bhūteṣu vicitya dhīrāḥ
pretyāsmāllokādamṛtā bhavanti // (KENOPANIṢAD : 2.5)

This mantra purports to say that a person who right now gets engrossed in righteous thinking and endeavours to know God, only he achieves success. On the other hand, if a person spends his life only in mundane activities, he is putting himself to great loss.

In this whole process there are also some very essential rules and precautions which must be observed by every sādhaka.

Special Rules and Precautions

- Observance of celibacy is most indispensable. A householder (gṛhastha) can also attain this supreme bliss through this effortless procedure of spiritual discipline. For the attainment of this absolute bliss he also will have to forsake momentary sensual pleasures, otherwise it will not be possible to rise to full elevation.

- Also pay attention to the purity and simplicity of food. Proper food, proper sleep and a disciplined life are the *sine qua non* of meditation and worship.
- Nobody can be a yogi without adhering to abstinences (yamas) and observances (niyamas). Therefore, in order to attain kuṇḍalinī-rising, complete cleansing and penetrating of cakras, and the state of samādhi, every seeker (sādhaka) must make all-out efforts to adhere to the five abstinences, viz. non-violence, speaking the truth, non-stealing, celibacy and non-greed, and the five observances, viz. purity and cleanliness, contentment, penance, study of scriptures and complete dedication to God. You should not feel overawed that because of your non- compliance with yamas (abstinences) and niyamas (observances), you will not be able to become a complete yogi; but that is not the case. Just keep doing the yogic procedures in accordance with the aforesaid method, and your life will be blessed with yoga. Your faith, belief and sincerity in yamas, niyamas like non-violence, truth, etc. will be so much strengthened that you will not feel like telling a lie, etc. You will never have any feeling of violence toward anybody. That is why yoga is said to be natural and spontaneous, yoga is our own religion.
- Once the kuṇḍalinī is awakened, it should not be assumed that it will always keep on awakening without any effort or practice. To achieve this, one must constantly have a healthy mind and healthy body, cleanliness, purity of diet and thoughts as well as non-attachment, otherwise one can lose the practice of meditation.
- While pursuing this path, seekers should eschew pretension and ostentation, and should cultivate the virtue of being calm, natural, devoid of pride and arrogance, and be of limited speech. One should not at all be hungry for applause, name, fame, etc.

SYMPTOMS AND BENEFITS OF KUṆḌALINĪ AWAKENING

The spiritual benefit of kuṇḍalinī-awakening is beyond words. However, it can be said without any doubt that it is a state of complete bliss. Nothing remains to be attained after attaining this state. There is complete contentment, serenity and supreme happiness. Another person sitting near such a sādhaka also experiences peace and serenity. By sitting near such a yogi all the agitations and distractions of the other person also start getting becalmed, and one develops faith and devotion toward yoga and God. Besides, one whose kuṇḍalinī is awakened develops the glow of grace and beauty in his body. A feeling of happiness and equanimity reflects from his face. Feelings of affection, compassion and divinity can be read in his eyes. His thinking becomes completely pure and sublime. In short, every aspect of his life touches the heights of sacredness, sublimity and greatness.

On one hand this whole process has its spiritual benefits, on the other, its great importance lies in the fact that a person practising these yogic procedures cannot suffer from any disease. Cancer, heart disease, diabetes, obesity, all stomach ailments, all imbalances and disorders of vāta, pitta and kapha are automatically eliminated. A person becomes completely healthy. Is it a small achievement for a selfish person of modern times that all his diseases can be eliminated without any medicine, and throughout his life he can remain hale and hearty, mentally sharp and work-efficient?

Normally a person is capable of utilizing only 5% of his physical, mental, intellectual and spiritual potential. With the awakening of kuṇḍalinī all his internal powers and inner intellect are awakened, and from an ordinary man he becomes a great man, an apostle, a prophet. Divine powers incarnate themselves in an accomplished yogi. God chooses such a yogi for the purpose of propagating peace and welfare in the world. Such a yogi lives as a representative of God, and millions of people repose their faith in him. He becomes the living embodiment of religiosity, spirituality, and God's existence.

LIST OF ŚLOKAS/MANTRAS